EFFECTIVE MANAGEMENT OF
RESEARCH AND DEVELOPMENT

EFFECTIVE MANAGEMENT OF RESEARCH AND DEVELOPMENT

P. A. F. WHITE, O.B.E., B. Sc., C. Eng., F. I. Mech. E., F. I. Chem. E.

First edition 1975
Second edition 1980

Published by
THE MACMILLAN PRESS LTD
London and Basingstoke
Associated companies in
Delhi Dublin Hong Kong
Johannesburg Lagos Melbourne
New York Singapore Tokyo

ISBN 0 333 28720 7

Photoset and printed in Great Britain by
REDWOOD BURN LIMITED
Trowbridge & Esher

Contents

Preface

The Research and Development scenario has undergone a substantial change over the last decade or so. From a setting in which total effort was expanding rapidly with a faith that more R & D was inevitably rewarding, has come the much more critical atmosphere in which, firstly, efforts were made to increase the productivity of research and, secondly, much greater perception of the necessity of fitting research to social needs has arisen.

The move towards quantifying or at least logical planning of research has become more refined while the relationship of R & D to 'marketability' factors has also assumed greater importance. Methods of inspiring creativity in relation to innovation have received much attention as have the nature of the structure of scientific organisations and methods of managing creative scientists.

This book is concerned with the situation as it appears now – with the rational tools available for assisting in management, with the many aspects of increasing efficiency and productivity in the laboratory and with the many factors which go to directing a successful R & D effort tuned to the needs of its parent authority from customer/contractor relationship to methods of structuring R & D organisations and management styles. Data related to expenditure on R & D in various fields is given for both the UK and the USA.

It may be that the refinement of the tools for such rationalisation of the management of R & D has sometimes misguided managers into forgetting that it is still the quality of the output of the front-line researchers which decides whether advances are feasible and this book continually emphasises the need for creating the right environment for researchers as the prime task of the R & D management.

Literature on the subject of R & D management was prolific about a decade ago, when the new quantifiable techniques were first gaining recognition but is harder to find in relation to the present outlook. This book is written largely from the author's experience as the Head of the Division of Chemical Technology at the UKAEA Aldermaston (now Ministry of

Defence) for the last sixteen years together with experience of industrial and civil service research before that, as well as from much of the literature of recent years.

It is felt that it is now timely for a book to appear on the present changed scenario. It is hoped that it will be of help to those already engaged in the managing and directing of research and to those who aspire to such a goal. It should also be of value to students in universities and polytechnics, particularly in the technological disciplines, who wish eventually to work in some field of applying research to practical problems or any others who seek a text for training in the wider issues of managing the application of research. Managers of other departments than the research department might find this book useful to tell themselves of the nature of the problems of their technical colleagues.

There are many people who have played a part indirectly in the production of this book – particularly the many staff at AWRE Aldermaston with whom the methods of managing large and small scale R & D enterprises were jointly forged over the years.

More directly I should particularly like to thank Dr J. W. Weale, Superintendent of Nuclear Physics at AWRE Aldermaston for help in methods of applying management by objectives in the research field; Mr R. L. Latham, Senior Superintendent, Engineering, at AWRE Aldermaston for help in relation to his own development of Problem Analysis by Logical Approach; Dr P. M. S. Jones, Head of the Programmes Analysis Unit, Chilcott, Harwell, for information regarding cost/benefit analysis studies; Mr A. J. Richards of the Department of Trade and Industry for up-to-date information about the industrial research associations; Mr C. J. Whapham of the Department of Industry for up-to-date information on Research Establishment data and Mr D. W. Baines of the Department of Education and Science for information regarding Research Council Research Stations.

Acknowledgement is also due to each of the following for permission to reproduce figures: Chapman & Hall Ltd (Figures 5.7–5.10), Her Majesty's Stationery Office (Figure 4.1), International Communications Ltd (Figure 7.1) and the United Kingdom Atomic Energy Authority (Figures 1.2 and 1.3).

1 Introduction

There are many different motives for doing research and development. Scientists are hired by organisations or indulge in the trade themselves, to make money, to solve practical problems, to satisfy curiosity, to improve the lot of mankind, whether in health or riches, to maintain the defence of their country, to improve the environment or simply to support a desire for prestige – personal, corporate or national. But for whatever reason it is conducted, research and development has become a big business in recent years. In Great Britain it absorbs about 2.7 per cent of the Gross National Product and occupies over a third of all persons holding degrees in engineering, technology or science or nearly 60,000 (outside education). [1] Nowadays hardly any research is carried out by private individuals and so all this effort is contained within Research and Development departments, institutes or establishments of one sort or another. Each of these has to be managed and directed with the distinction between management and direction dependent on the size and environment of the working group. In general it is true that a group of graduates about 10–20 strong will need to be supervised by someone who will be at least partly involved in the management of the group in relation to higher policy. Such a group may well be part of a larger group of say 40–60 graduates, the supervision of which will involve further management and directing skills. Still larger groups, of course, also occur and in these a heirarchy of people with different directing functions at different levels is likely to obtain.

On such a basis we can see that there are approaching 6,000 people involved in the management and direction of research and development in the UK. It is with the activities of such executives that this book is involved. It may be of interest to some who are already performing jobs of this nature and perhaps even more so to those who expect to be moving up to this level. It should not be without interest to many research workers themselves to learn something of the problems their seniors are involved in. Indeed, there is a great deal to be said for all prospective workers in the R & D field to have a greater knowledge of the problems of using research towards practical ends and pressure has been building up recently for universities and polytechnics to make available courses based on the principles involved. This book may provide a useful text for such courses.

One other category of reader intended is the non-technical director or manager who is interested to know something of the problems that beset his technical colleagues, and comments on the relationships between research and engineering and sales for example have been included.

UNIQUE CHARACTERISTICS OF R & D MANAGEMENT

Research and development have several unique characteristics which make the problems of their management different from other management problems. Among these are:

(a) The processes and activities are constantly changing both for the individual worker and for the organisation as a whole.

(b) The staff is unusual in its originality and enquiring nature and in its allegiance to a discipline outside any that the organisation requires.

(c) Allied to this is the fact that a career in science has its own stability, but the stability of most scientific jobs is not great. The organisation therefore has continually to supply assignments of the right challenge to maintain its staff.

(d) The evaluation of the results of research is difficult and criteria for success of departments or individuals difficult to establish.

(e) A research department must engender a pattern of professional equals amongst its staff, whatever the rank of the disputants.

CHANGING NATURE OF RESEARCH MANAGEMENT

As in most spheres of human activity, the outlook and the tasks of the research director of the seventies are different from those of previous decades. Only twenty years ago directors of research tended to be themselves outstanding researchers assisted by teams in work which was chosen mainly on a basis of personal judgement or even inclination, although related to the objectives of the organisation in which they were working. They worked against the background that during the first decade after the Second World War research efforts could be directed towards any number of products and processes within an organisation's field and be expected to reap benefits to that organisation without questions being asked about how effective they were. The sixties drew gradually increasing attention to the efficiency and productivity of research and development both in the selection of topics and in methods of operation. This took place in an atmosphere generated by scarcity of science graduates and severe questioning of the costs of research, both nationally and in individual organisations. It was also a period in which it was almost mythically assumed that more and more research meant more and more productivity and profitability. So it became important to get a maximum of research out of a limited work force with a minimum of expenditure.

Now in the seventies there is the even keener question of why we should do research at all, reflecting an anxiety that basic research grows beyond the powers of society to use it while application or technological research is not sufficiently fast or effective to meet the needs of a technological society, whether these be considered as further industrial growth or the improvement of the quality of life in other directions. It is also a time when there is doubt both about the correlation between research and invention and about research as the road to industrial growth.

JUSTIFICATION OF R & D

It is thus being increasingly asked whether organisations are getting a good return from the substantial investment they are risking on innovation. The number of patents issued in proportion to R & D expenditure has been falling, and while there are many explanations for this trend, it does nevertheless raise the question of how productive innovative effort is becoming. The experience organisations have had with research programmes has not always been a happy one. Jewkes, Sawers and Stillerman in a survey of recent trends [2] conclude that many large companies are adjusting the approach to R & D. They are now more frequently to be heard stressing the benefits of sometimes being second in the field, of buying in new ideas from outside, or even of buying up smaller companies which have already carried out the pioneering work on new developments.[3] It is unfortunate that this should happen at a time when more and more science and technology graduates are available. It can hardly be doubted, however, that properly directed project-orientated research is still an unparalleled tool for achieving many of the aims of industry and society in the material sense. Indeed it has been estimated for instance that technical change contributed about four times more than capital accumulation to the growth of output per head in the US from 1909 to 1949 apart from farming.[46]

So the research manager of today is primarily concerned that research should only be done where it is effective to the aims of the organisation of which it is part, that what is done should be done creatively, efficiently and with a maximum of productivity and that the results of the research should be exploited either internally to the organisation or externally, to the maximum of benefit. It is still highly desirable that his team should have some evidence of his own research ability, although he appears in the laboratories less and less and at a conference table more and more. Instead of acting as a creative research worker he tends more and more to act as an interface – hopefully a creative interface – between the researchers and higher policy-making executives.

To carry out this task involves close attention to, and the use of techniques for, the development of good research aims, the provision of an environment in which they can be actively pursued, the organisation of effective management with adequate tools to ensure they can operate efficiently, and the development of sensitive controls and techniques of feedback to inform and influence higher management actions and policy. It is with these problems and methods of attacking them that this book is concerned. It is not intended as a handbook so that many techniques will be but briefly outlined (though references to more detailed descriptions will be given), but rather as a guide to the attitudes and interests that need to be developed for the best use of R & D. It does not seek to describe the conduct of research, although a research manager will be very concerned that the research in his department is being conducted on sound lines.

Research projects usually involve numbers of man years of intellectual effort. It is expensive in many terms (with laboratory facilities, assistants and normal overhead charges a professional man – year now costs about £14,000 in a reasonably sophisticated laboratory), but it is even more expensive in the sense of using high grade intellectual ability – a limited commodity in any country. The final decision on whether to make use of such a man year of work, or how to make use of it may become a matter almost of man minutes to a research director. What sort of thinking and working are required before the project is initiated and during its pursuit before those decisive man minutes of reckoning. Research management is successful only if nearly every project has its use and as many as possible have a very high gain factor in the field of interest that higher management is responsible for.

This is the essence of the job of a research manager. The principles used in exercising such jobs are much the same in large organisations or small, whether the R & D is done in government establishments, research association laboratories, sponsored research institutes, or industrial firms. It is probably even true of university research so long as it is borne in mind that gain factors are then related to the aims of pure science and of teaching.

MEANING OF RESEARCH AND DEVELOPMENT

The term Research and Development has been endlessly defined and the differences between pure research, applied research, project-orientated research and development debated and misunderstood equally so. In the author's view much work is termed pure research which should be termed project-orientated. We have not yet rid outselves in this country of the habit of thinking that pure research is somehow superior to applied research so people like to call their work pure research or pure science. It can, however, be argued that much basic research can be imitative, repetitive and poor in quality while much project-orientated work can be highly imaginative and original in itself. It can also be argued that project-orientated research and development using as they do the research method within the constraints of desired end points, time schedules and financial considerations offer at least as great a challenge to the intellect, while demanding other powers of organisation and awareness which make it altogether a superior activity.

There are four broad bands of research activity which need to be recognised as having different natures, although they will overlap and merge from one into the other and one cannot be simply classified as superior to another.

First, in the sense that it is likely to precede the others in time-scale, is basic research. The main characteristic of this is that it is not subject to a time-restraint, at least not in relation to a project requirement, and that it is open ended, in the sense that the researcher is merely seeking to see where his research takes him. Basic research can be completely free or it might be confined to some area of activity when it might be termed underlying or mission-orientated basic research. Thus work at AERE Harwell on the effect of neutron irradiation on materials is carried out in order to develop understanding of a subject which should prove of value in the development of nuclear reactors.

Second, and closely allied to underlying basic research, is exploratory research in which there is an objective – the researcher might be looking for a new drug and examining the biological effects of a new range of chemical materials – but the research is nevertheless open ended in the sense that one is looking for something which might form the basis for a successful project development.

Third, there is technological research, or applied research or objective research or project-orientated research. This is where the previous research has led to an innovatory idea but research is required to test its scientific feasibility, the reproducibility of results, to improve the results from a 'market' point of view, in fact to take the discovery to a point where its likely viability as a 'marketable' object can be established. Concurrent with this stage, there will in fact be a preliminary study of 'costs' and 'markets' and the result of the combined activity will be to furnish evidence for the senior management to decide whether or not to go ahead with development.

Fourth, there is development in which research methods continue to be used to take a process or product, which is basically understood, up to a point of practical use whether it be a process which can operate at full industrial scale such as the fast breeder reactor or a product which will be saleable or useable for some social need such as an artificial heart. It does not always apply that the phases of research activity follow each other through the spectrum. A fundamental idea may be sufficiently complete and useful in itself that it can be straight away applied to a practical operation. On the other hand a development programme may be well under way before it is realised that there is a need for some fundamental research. The development activity is, however, closely related to and integrated with the design function and to the use of existing information, but its outstanding characteristic is the influence on it of time and money. For the decision to proceed with the development stage is financially the most important in the R & D sequence. Before the decision is made the amount of money spent is relatively small, as is the involvement of staff and facilities outside the research department, and the dependence of a successful outcome on the time taken is small or at least cannot be greatly hurried. After the development project is born the development engineer enters the picture alongside the research scientist whom he will sooner or later replace in the management of the project: market research and marketing arrangements have to be geared to the expected end product and time of completion: the amount of money involved will go up considerably (the ratio of development cost to research cost is likely to be as much as 10:1). Up to the development stage, the research is subject to 'tech-

8

nological push'. The development stage is dominated by 'managerial pull'.[4 and 5]

Time is usually an overriding consideration. With the increasing complexity of modern technology it is often true that the lead time (time taken to lead through R & D to the successful product) for developing new systems is often longer than their useful life whether the objective be military or commercial and the less the lead time, the greater the useful life which justifies the expenditure on the research. Money is an important consideration for it is the development stage which includes the building of the prototype and first 'commercial' models and 'market' trials of one sort or another.

PLACE OF R & D IN CASH FLOW OF A PROJECT

Fig. 1 shows a cash flow diagram for a typical new chemical process. It shows the significant change in expenditure at the development stage and indicates that the completion of development leads to even greater expenditure on full-scale plant and start up, after which the financial returns begin to come in. A period of maximum profitability follows which is all too soon succeeded by a period of diminishing profitability. The earlier the development can be completed and the plant built the longer is likely to be the period of acceptable profitability.[5]

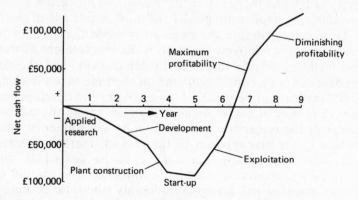

FIG. 1.1 Cash flow diagram of research project leading to commercial exploitation

INVENTION AND INNOVATION

It is important to distinguish between invention, which is the end product of research, and innovation which follows invention and is the end point of successful development. 'Invention implies bringing something new into being: innovation implies bringing something new into use.'[6]

The total process of innovation has a number of stages linking inputs of expenditure and manpower with outputs of new products or processes. These may be analysed as:[7]

1. Stimulus – whereby a company or organisation is provoked by some need into expressing the requirement of a new idea and a member of the organisation gives expression to a new idea – he might do research to get it, or obtain it by external contacts.

2. Conception – a plan of action to give the idea form is conceived.

3. Proposal – a formal proposal is put forward to senior management.

4. Adoption – the proposal is accepted as something for the organisation to make its business, after appropriate specialists have appraised the proposal.

5. Implementation – by going through the stages to 'bring it to the market'.

In this analysis, the first three stages represent invention while the last two represent innovation if they reach a successful end point, adopted by society.

This distinction between invention and innovation assumes importance when considering problems of organisation, staff management, etc. as will be discussed in subsequent chapters.

CHIEF ACTIVITIES OF AN R & D DEPARTMENT

Bearing these definitions in mind, the activities of a typical R & D establishment will involve:

(a) Pure research – to a small extent for a better understanding of the basis of some of the activities of an organisation, e.g. distillation in an oil firm.

(b) Exploratory research and mission-orientated research to

(1) discover new products within the framework of the organisation's responsibilities.

(2) test the feasibility of practical use of a discovery.

(3) improve the efficiency of the organisation's existing operations.

(4) change the base of an industrial or other effort, e.g. petro-chemicals, atomic explosives.

(5) solve the problems of raw materials shortages, energy restrictions, pollution from the firm's operations.

(c) Development – for bringing to fruition or optimising any of the objectives of technological research.

(d) The application of existing scientific knowledge to the problems of the organisation.

(e) Extra-mural activities of many types.

(1) Research carried out at universities, research associations, sponsored research institutes.

(2) Research taken in from outside organisations.

(3) Maintaining contact with research associations, universities, consultants, government departments.

In one sense, the most important of these is the technological research function in that choice of a development project will depend on the skill with which this is carried out as will the successful solution of the organisation's many technical problems. It is not possible to develop what is not fundamentally sound and to develop a process which cannot show a substantial cost or social advantage is not a productive way of using research effort. The heavy spending development activity is greatly dependent on successful technological research.

EFFECT OF ORGANISATIONAL AIMS ON BALANCE OF EFFORT

The balance of effort between these activities in different departments or establishments will vary greatly depending upon the aims of the organisation concerned. In a typical chemical plant constructing organisation, for instance, very little research might be done because the tendency might be to buy processes from other countries or firms so that only optimisation to meet customer requirements is required of the R & D department. In a research association, on the other hand, more research might be done, leaving the development to optimisation to the industrial members of the association. In a university far more basic research might be expected than any other but even here the full spectrum of activities will be observed, particularly in departments of physical sciences, technology and engineering and in the technological universities where objectives are sought and research orientated towards them as anxiously as in many industrial firms. In fact equal amounts of basic and applied research are recorded for universities in HMSO *Statistics of Science and Technology*.[1]

Each R & D establishment (and the different types will be discussed more fully later) therefore contains a different mix of these same ingredients. Their direction will equally have many aspects in common. A typical example of the make-up of work-pattern and its gradual change over the years is shown in Fig. 1.2. In this is shown the effect at AERE Harwell of a reduction in the requirements of the nuclear energy business for basic research and the wish of the Government for a scale down of the total effort on Government nuclear contracts partly counter-balanced by pick-up of extramural work on a repayment basis. The analysis of this repayment work is shown in Fig. 1.3.[3]

THE MANAGEMENT ROLE

It has been said by the late Professor Bernal that running a research establishment is like running a gambling concern and taking incalculable risks for unassessable rewards. It is in the nature of research that this should remain true to a substantial extent. The manager's role, however, is to minimise the risk and maximise the reward. He has to do this while poised between the enthusiastic efforts of perhaps large numbers of researchers whose sense of creative freedom has to be maintained and the more prosaic demands of profitability or effectiveness of his sponsors.

His principal task will be to establish project areas which

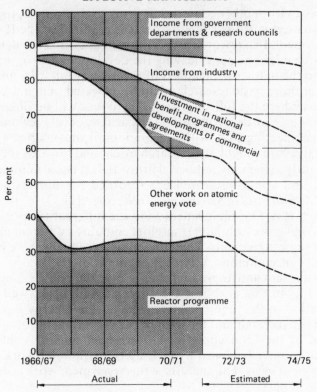

FIG. 1.2 AERE Harwell – Analysis of financing of work [8]

will best serve the interests of his organisation. These have to be related to the abilities and needs of his staff or the staff he can hope to recruit and to financial limits that are imposed on him. When these project areas are generated his task will be to see that programmes are evolved for carrying them through, with a minimum of research effort and a maximum use of existing knowledge both inside and outside his department or organisation and the exercise of judgement between them. As a corollary he has to ensure that all his staff have some effective work to do. In this way his research and development programmes are built up into a portfolio of activities. They then have to be guided to ensure that they remain tuned to the project objectives, its time scales and financial constraints. Atten-

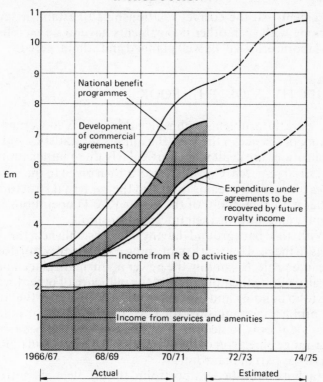

£m

FIG. 1.3 Analysis of financing of Harwell's industrial and other repayment work[8]

tion has to be paid to assure the most efficient conduct of research and the utmost productivity from it. Finally he has to ensure that the end result of the research is presented adequately for maximum use to be made of it and exploited to the full. He has to establish a style of management which will confer a degree of freedom, substantial job satisfaction and continued enthusiasm among his research workers. That useful training of staff is undertaken when necessary will be a continuing concern, as will questions of the safety of the operations under his control. Research can only be usefully carried out if it is well serviced by engineers and technicians and if it relates to other activities such as design and 'customer' requirements, so the correct relationships to establish smooth working with such other departments have to be established. His laboratories will be well planned and administered.

OBJECTIVES OF THE BOOK

These are the problems with which this book is concerned. The picture of science in the UK, the important statistics and their implications are dealt with, particularly those implications for industrial research. Consideration is then given to the different types of research organisation and their internal structure, together with an account of the major R & D operations in the country and showing their interrelationship.

With this background having been established the book turns to the problems of establishing a satisfactory portfolio of research projects – noting the newer mathematical techniques, but also noting their pitfalls and the influence of other forces in portfolio building and bearing in mind particularly that one of the primary prerequisites for effective discharge of management's duties is to acquire and maintain a clear view of the long-range objectives of the enterprise as a whole and of R & D activity as part of that whole.

Having established the portfolio, the problem of controlling the research activities carried out within them is next dealt with. Again the modern techniques are reviewed, but with some caution regarding their too thorough application.

Means by which productivity can be increased in the R & D department both directly in efficient experimentation and by the most efficient use of direct services to the researchers is then dealt with.

The special problems related to staff selection, management and development are an additional important facet in the operation of a successful research department, as are also the operation of indirect services such as the information and library services. These matters are discussed, not so much from the point of view of how they should be planned, but from the point of view of features of them which are important to successful research. The place of the human sciences is also discussed.

There is also a section on laboratory planning and administration which is not usually given due recognition for its importance in the efficient conduct of research.

In conclusion, the problems of leadership in a research department towards the end of obtaining creativity and professional dedication to successful results are considered. For it must not be overlooked that the prime job of management in a research department must be to develop creative thinking in the scientific staff and imbue a sense of logical thinking and resourceful experimentation towards the desired objective: for it is creative scientific thinking in the long run rather than good management and efficiency which will determine the real success of R & D operations. Creative people should be supervised by creative people and the creative nature of the research management function is stressed throughout this book.

PAY-OFF OF IMPROVED MANAGEMENT

The pay-off from sound management is large. If research could be costed to give only a 10 : 1 benefit/cost ratio then the estimated £1000m spent on R & D in the UK alone could earn the country £1000m per year, if management were improved to achieve only a 10 per cent increase in research effectiveness. Even the research unit with a budget of £100,000 per year would yield its parent authority £100,000 a year extra with management improvement of the same order. These are conservative figures and in many research departments the effectiveness could be increased by much larger factors.

SUMMARY

Research and development have become a big business, accounting for about 2.7 per cent of the Gross National Product. Nearly all of it is carried out in research departments which need managing and directing, the functions that this book deals with. It should be of interest to researchers themselves, junior and senior managers and directors, post graduate students in technological departments and to directors of other aspects of technological enterprises.

Research and development have several unique characteristics relating to the ever-changing nature of their processes, the particular attributes of scientific staff and the difficulty of assessing results.

Research management has changed substantially over the last few decades with attention presently focused on only carrying out research if it makes a serious contribution to the goals of the parent authority, and then to carry it out with the greatest efficiency.

The four phases of research are described: basic research, exploratory research, mission-orientated research and development with particular reference to the changes attendant on moving to the development phase. Invention and innovation are distinguished and typical operations of a research department are discussed with reference to the changing work-patterns which they undergo.

The management role in such undertakings is described in relation to the remaining contents of the book.

The pay-off from sound R & D management is reflected in the saving occurring in a £100,000 a year budget if a 10 per cent improvement is obtained with research which yields a 10 : 1 benefit cost advantage; for £100,000/year would then be the improvement in benefit obtained.

2 General considerations of R & D activities

Research and development can best be effectively carried out with a background knowledge of what is going on outside the immediate activities of an R & D department. The researcher himself must know what scientific work has been published and what is being presently conducted in so far as this is available to him relative to his own work; the manager must be aware of the nature of the operations of the organisation for which the R & D is being carried out as well as having a wide knowledge of the scientific background to the work of his group; the director should additionally be aware of the scenario of R & D on a national or even an international scale so that he can bring to bear on the operations of his department those activities which will make them more fruitful and more efficient.

Until the late 1960s the great emphasis of science application was on increasing the wealth of the country by growth in the national economy but forces were developing strongly in the early 1970s to re-orientate research to a greater degree in the direction of 'improving the quality of life'. This gives new impetus to the applied social sciences, but it has also renewed the remit of the material sciences in the direction of eliminating the pollution and increasing the safety of technological operations and conserving materials and energy resources. Government is more constrained to create policy and regulations towards these ends and to place development contracts appropriately. These tendencies are likely to be increasingly widely interpreted – thus conservation includes the preservation of food by lyophilisation, deep freezing, sterilisation and pest control. Also the scientist-manager will find himself increasingly in the situation of using his forces as an element in multi-disciplinary teams with economists, psychologists, etc. in attacking problems in which the needs of society provide the 'pull' rather than pure science providing the push.[9]

This chapter is concerned with some general considerations relating to wider concepts of R & D including a general picture of expenditure and staff usage in the country and reference to some of the studies of the conduct of R & D as an economic activity.

TOTAL NATIONAL EXPENDITURE ON R & D

The total annual expenditure on research and development in Great Britain, as expressed as a percentage of gross national product is shown in the graph of Fig. 1. [1, 10 and 11]

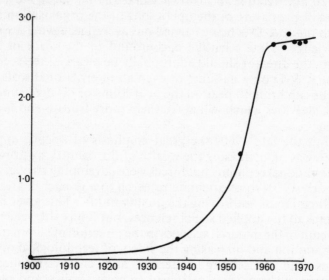

FIG. 2.1 Growth of R & D expenditure in UK in the twentieth century

It will be seen that at the beginning of the century only a minute R & D effort existed, which expanded but modestly until a great upsurge took place between 1940 and 1960, since when it has become almost constant as a fraction of GNP. Actual expenditure has continued to increase, figures since

1961/62 being approximately as shown in Table 2.1. [1 and 11] The national product, in real terms, has increased by about a quarter over this eight-year period, so that a more or less constant share of the total, spent on R & D, is not inconsistent with a fairly large expansion of such R & D work.

TABLE 2.1 COST OF R & D IN THE UNITED KINGDOM

	£m
1961/62	677
1964/65	791
1966/67	926
1967/68	962
1969/70	1082

Undoubtedly the upsurge from 1938 was occasioned first by war conditions and then by the growing appreciation by government and industry of the success in practical problems which applied research could achieve.

The present figure of 2.7 per cent of GNP for the United Kingdom compares with other countries as shown in Table 2.2. [12]

TABLE 2.2   R & D EFFORT IN TERMS OF GNP IN DIFFERENT COUNTRIES

	R & D expenditure as percentage of GNP for 1963–64	Average/annum rate of growth of GNP 1960–70
Japan	1.5	11.3
Southern European countries	0.2	6.7
Italy	0.7	5.7
France	1.9	5.6
Canada	1.2	4.9
West Germany	1.6	4.7
United States	3.7	4.2
United Kingdom	2.7	2.7

It will be seen from this that the UK occupies a high place in its rate of spending on R & D.

However, it would appear that technologically advancing

countries with low research spends are now accelerating such spends dramatically, as shown by recent figures issued by the National Science Foundation, USA, shown in Table 2.3. [83]

TABLE 2.3   R & D SPENDING PATTERNS OF SELECTED COUNTRIES 1967–71

	Relative growth in R & D expenditure	
	1967	1971
United States	100	116
France	100	127
United Kingdom	100	121
Japan	100	247
Germany	100	189

Furthermore, recent figures on actual expenditure of different countries are given by Rothschild [13] and quoted in Table 2.4.

As Rothschild says, it is an unanswerable question as to whether we are right to spend less than France and whether a better comparison could be obtained by suitably weighting the figures by factors depending on population, stage of industrial development, etc. We cannot even be sure whether an increase in GNP is caused by an increase in R & D (the evidence of Table 2.2 would suggest that it may not be) or whether, under certain circumstances, an increase in prosperity in a country causes an increase in R & D. It is certainly noticeable that Japan with the fastest rate of growth spends appreciably less on R & D than many other countries of slower rate of growth.

The slow down in the rate of increase of expenditure on R & D in the United Kingdom since 1960 is a reflection of the growing concern over such data, the greater concern for efficiency and productivity of research and, indeed the growing concern about many implications of the R & D explosion.

The report of the Council for Scientific Policy 1972 records a sharp decline in rate of growth of the Research Councils from 13 per cent in 1966/67 to 4 per cent in 1972/73 and indicates an expected further diminution by 1974/75 to below 2 per cent.

The present national position is, therefore, one of doubt as to what the correct overall expenditure on research and development should be, with arguments for the necessity of tailoring expenditure more to the economic processes of the country countered by the pleas of pure scientists for an ever-increasing expenditure.

TABLE 2.4   PUBLIC EXPENDITURE ON R & D IN VARIOUS COUNTRIES
(*1970 Figures except where stated*)

	Total £m	Civil £m
United States (1969)	6,652	3,393
Germany	725	600
France	735	510
United Kingdom	581	353
Japan	351	344
Italy	191	185
Netherlands	128	122
Belgium	52	50

EXPENDITURE BY DIFFERENT SECTORS

The total spend in 1969–70 of £1082m aggregates the cost of research and development carried out by different major sections of the country's economy as shown in Table 2.5 column A, expressed as percentage in column B.

TABLE 2.5   R & D SPEND IN THE UNITED KINGDOM 1969–70

	(A) Carried out in each sector £m	(B) Percentage	(C) Finance supplied by each sector £m	(D) Percentage
Government				
Defence	104.8	9.7	230.0	21.3
Civil	110.9	10.3	249.0	23.0
Research councils	46.9	4.3	79.8	7.4
Sub-total	262.7	24.3	558.8	51.7
Universities and further education establishments	91.1	8.4	6.8	0.6
Public corporations	44.9	4.2	51.7	4.8
Research associations	16.5	1.5	0.1	
Private industry	636.1	58.8	409.5	37.9
Others	30.6	2.8	55.0	5.0
Total	1081.9	100.0	1081.9	100.0

It is important to note that much of the R & D performed by one sector, as indicated in column A, is financed by another, usually by the placing of contracts for R & D to be carried out, or by the making of grants. In column C is shown the actual funding on R & D of the different national sectors and this will include the money spent on R & D within the sector and in support of other sectors. Column D expresses these figures as percentages.

It will be seen that about a quarter of all R & D is carried out by the government who indeed finance research to the extent of over half the total expenditure, while the private industry share of financing is at about 38 per cent although nearly 60 per cent of all R & D is carried out by industry.

This is a pattern which has persisted from the early 1960s except that a decline in government defence expenditure has been balanced by a rise in government civil research and development (including atomic energy). This trend is shown by the records given in Table 2.6 for government expenditure in 1966/67 compared with 1969/70.

TABLE 2.6 CENTRAL GOVERNMENT EXPENDITURE ON
SCIENTIFIC RESEARCH AND DEVELOPMENT [11]
(*Gross expenditure*)

	1966–67	£1000	1969–70
Defence	279,738		253,790
Civil			
Research councils	63,174		87,737
Trade and industry	126,467		179,424
Agriculture, fisheries and forests	6,876		13,191
Housing and environment	220		857
Health and Welfare	3,435		5,448
Roads and transport	2,931		4,649
Law and order	172		606
Common services	5,192		7,035
Miscellaneous services	886		2,534
External relations	2,021		2,416
Government of N. Ireland	1,159		1,451
UK universities	41,790		56,000
Social science	2,281		5,095
Total civil	256,604		366,443

It represents, however, an even greater change from the mid fifties when over 60 per cent of all R & D was spent on government defence work either in government laboratories or by the government in private industry. Of course, government only spends money in those industries and other research and development establishments which deal in products or services of value to government and, in fact, this applied to relatively few industrial and other activities. But clearly it is widening because of the increasing R & D expenditure by government in the fields of transport, agriculture, health and welfare, financial administration, environmental problems, etc. Indeed, more than half of government civil expenditure on R & D is for work outside government or the Research Council's own establishments.

The importance of this to any organisation practising science outside government's own laboratories lies in the opportunities given by association with government activities. For by carrying out R & D for government agencies an organisation is on the one hand put in touch with the large body of sophisticated research conducted by government departments and on the other hand put in touch with future markets to which the research effort should lead. So it would appear to be a desirable though not always possible aim that the R & D portfolio of an organisation should include some government sponsored work. (See also Chapter 4.)

The question of how much money should be spent in government laboratories and how much further the swing to using government money to finance research outside government laboratories should go is exercising a great deal of attention at this time.

Some would argue that the research should be carried out to a greater extent at or near the centres of production (mainly industry) since the country's major need is for competitive production for the economic health of the nation. In simple terms industry knows what is wanted to make it more competitive.

The opposing argument is that industry is reluctant to spend the large sums of money required for really high gain factor improvements and is inclined to restrict its projects to those which are relatively short term, safe and aimed at fairly modest advances in its art.

Professor Mansfield, working in the United States, [14] a country with a high reputation for progress in industrial innovation, studied that question in relation to the central laboratory of a large electronic corporation and concluded that 'it appears that most projects are expected to be completed in 4 years or less and results to be applied only a few months later and the estimated probability of technical success averages about 0.80'. R.E. Seiler would go further and reports [15] 'The duration of the average [R & D] project throughout American industry appears to be approximately 13–24 man-months, but this is a matter of breakdown convenience and some are recorded as 1000 man-months.'

It is certainly difficult to imagine atomic energy being developed by industry alone, however heavily financed by government, by such a philosophy.

The importance of this to the director of R & D, however, is that such movements of government policy deserve to be studied so that the future opportunities for fruitful research projects are appreciated.

EXPENDITURE IN UNIVERSITIES AND RESEARCH ASSOCIATIONS

From Table 2.5 it will also be noted that the universities and other further education establishments are now carrying out R & D to the extent of over £90m per year although only £6.8m of this is provided by the universities themselves. Again the main supplier of funds is the government with £75m, with industry only supplying £4m. [1] As we have noted in Chapter 1 half of university research work is of an applied character but inevitably universities are likely to be concerned with new concepts. In fact university research represents one of the most rapidly expanding areas of research in the country, as indicated by the attached graph Fig. 2.2.

The importance of university research to an R & D organisation outside the university is twofold. Firstly it can give the initial indications of what are likely to be important scientific ideas worthy of eventual development and application, and secondly associated with it are people who can present knowledgeable but fresh minds to the problems of an organisation. There is, therefore, a lot to be said for any R & D organisation developing close contacts with university departments appropriate to its work (See Chapter 4). The growth of university research work makes this more significant. It is surprising that private industry uses such a small amount of its budget for this purpose. It would appear further to support the Mansfield thesis that industry is sometimes not as mindful of long-term basic ideas as it might be.

More will be written about research associations in Chapter 4 but it will be seen from Table 2.5 that expenditure in such establishments, serving as they do practically the whole of industry, is very small indeed.

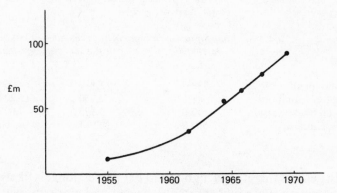

FIG. 2.2 Cost of R & D in universities and further education establishments

COST PER PROFESSIONAL SCIENTIST

Table 2.7 compares the cost per graduate per year in different research sectors for 1967/68. [1] This would give us figures of £19,000 in government research, £14,600 in industry and £7,000 in research associations. A number of factors contribute to such costs, principally the extent and sophistication of facilities and research aids, the numbers of assistants, both technical and industrial, and the overheads imposed by the organisation in which the work is carried out. Equally the necessity of expensive facilities and large numbers of assistants will depend on the type of work being carried out. Thus, chemical research is unlikely to be as expensive in these aids as mechanical engineering. As will be discussed elsewhere, however, good facilities and adequate assistance are likely to attract better research workers and enable them to be more productive. Also more sophisticated and expensive facilities are likely to be associated either with a greater depth of scientific work or, so far as technological research is concerned, with operations at substantial pilot plant or prototype engineering stages which are closer to major advances in real process innovation.

TABLE 2.7   R & D SPEND FOR 1967–68 COMPARED WITH GRADUATES EMPLOYED ON R & D

Sector	Value of research carried out £m	Number of graduates on R & D	Cost per graduate £/yr
Government	238.6	12,517	19,000
Public corporations	41.6	2,750	15,200
Research associations	13.0	1,973	7,000
Private industry	569.8	38,914	14,600

In general therefore a high spend per professional is likely to be associated with higher quality, deeper and more innovative research or research being carried further into areas of practical realisation.

RESEARCH IN INDUSTRY

As we have seen from Table 2.5 some 60 per cent of all R & D expenditure is carried out by private industry although only less than 37 per cent is funded by industry with the great majority of the rest coming from government.

The use by industry of R & D is, however, by no means uniform, as is shown in Table 2.8 which gives the expenditure on

TABLE 2.8 RESEARCH AND DEVELOPMENT CARRIED OUT WITHIN INDUSTRY IN THE UK

Product group	(A) Expenditure in 1969–70 (£1000)	(B) R & D employment of graduates 1968	(C)	(D) Expenditure % of turnover in selected industries	(E) % Qualified staff of total employed
Food, drink and tobacco	21,641	1,373	1	0.6	0.7
Chemical and allied industries	} 104,490	8,677	7	4.8	5.2
Mineral oil refining		863	12	—	1.3
Metal manufacture	18,171	1,755		0.9	1.3
Mechanical engineering (including scientific instruments)	77,638	5,063		2.0	1.9
Electrical engineering, electronics	182,904	10,540	5 } 20	6.8	4.4
Aircraft	169,945	4,323	39	35.1	3.0
Motor vehicles	48,937	858		} 1.7	0.7
Other vehicles	2,699	191			1.6
Textiles, clothing, etc.	17,059	1,726		0.5	0.5
Other manufacturing industries	—	2,940		1.8	0.6
Construction	3,127	—		0.1	

R & D carried out within different sectors of industry in 1969/70 (Column A) and the numbers of graduates employed in R & D in those sectors (Column B). [1 and 11]

In the table are shown figures for the R & D expenditure expressed as a percentage of turnover in selected industries, Column C for 1969 [16] compared with Column D [17] for 1955; Column E gives the density of qualified scientists in industrial sectors as a percentage of all employees. [18]

The general pattern of industrial science that emerges from such statistics is that science is predominantly an activity of a restricted group of industries, aircraft, chemicals, and electrical/electronic engineering. These are the industries which spend the largest amounts of money, employ the largest numbers of graduate scientists, and spend the highest proportions of their total turnover.

There is an intermediate group of industries such as mechanical engineering which are no doubt influenced by the predominant group, as suppliers to them. But for all others covering what are usually termed the traditional industries such as food, textiles, clothing, wood, printing, leather, paper, etc. science is not such a highly rated contributor.

Consideration of changes that have taken place over the last ten years, however, lends optimism to the view that many of the more traditional industries are making considerable efforts to improve their scientific position.

Finance for industrial R & D comes from various sources apart from government (nearly three-quarters of aerospace R & D in 1968/69 was financed by government as was two-fifths of R & D in the electronics industry). Some sectors receive significant amounts of R & D finance from abroad, usually from overseas parent or associate companies, the oil, pharmaceuticals and non-ferrous metals sectors all receiving nearly 10 per cent of their R & D funds from abroad.

Making allowances for external contributions, it appears that about 10 per cent net output is about the maximum from internal resources alone for any industrial sector.

Of course the functions and techniques of different industries are so different that one would not expect them all to have the same pattern of research effort. Some of the factors producing differences between industries are:

(a) Carrying out government work. Industries largely concerned with working for the government in defence and other advanced technological projects would themselves need to be technologically advanced.

(b) Importance of developing new products or processes. In an industry where new products and processes can greatly affect the performance and efficiency of the customer there will be a continual striving to innovate and science will be a necessary activity. This is particularly true of the chemical and electronics industries for whose customers a second-best product might have very little value. In some activities, however, product performance is of secondary importance, the customer does not ask for anything better technically so innovating activity is not energised.

(c) The ease with which R & D can lead to significant improvements. Industries working in spheres where there is a large background of fundamental research going on in the universities of a type which does not require large capital facilities for further development are likely to be keen to provide the relatively small investment required for improvement. Therein lies a weakness for it means that industry will be reluctant to tackle the more important revolutionary developments which might pay much bigger dividends but which require large investment in fundamental research as well as expensive development.

(d) Market structure. An industry that is composed of large numbers of small firms (e.g. house building) is unlikely to do much R & D. A firm which is in a near monopoly position relative to a static market is unlikely to do much R & D. Some industries like the chemical plant construction industry, tend to license processes and plant units rather than carry out their own R & D.

(e) Attitudes to change, of management, workers and public. Clearly where management is aggressive, relations with workers are flexible to changing work patterns and public reaction to a firm's products are not to insist on the traditional, the right environment for R & D and innovation will exist.

EFFECT OF SIZE OF FIRM

It is commonly agreed that a firm requires to have an annual turnover of more than £250,000 if it is to benefit from setting up its own laboratory. [5] Since the lowest cost of a graduate scientist with appropriate services is seen (Table 2.7) to be about £7,000 even this would represent 2.4 per cent of turnover which, as we have seen, would be a very high rate except for a specialised industry.

However, the overwhelming proportion of research and development is done by large firms: in terms of expenditure firms with 2000 or more employees account for more than 90 per cent of the total effort. While only 10 per cent of large firms report that they do not employ any qualified scientists on R & D, 45 per cent of medium-sized (300–2000 employees) and 80 per cent of small-sized firms so report.

So we have a general pattern of decreasing R & D effort with decreasing size. [36]

Mansfield [14] has carried out a series of detailed studies of the effect of the size of a firm as related to its research and development effort, leading to the following conclusions:

(a) Contrary to popular belief the inventive output per dollar of R & D expenditure in most cases seems to be lower in the largest firms than in large and medium-sized firms.

(b) However, although by no means universally true, the largest firms accounted for a larger share of the innovations than they did of the market, particularly where large investment relative to size of potential buyers obtained and as the years pass this becomes more so.

(c) When the size of a firm is held constant the number of significant inventions carried out by a firm seems to be strongly influenced by the size of its R & D expenditures. There seems to be a positive relationship over the long run between the amount a firm spends on research and the total number of important inventions it produces.

(d) When the size of a firm is held constant the evidence appears to suggest that increases in R & D expenditures result in more than proportional increases in inventive output in the chemical industry. In petroleum and steel the results do not indicate any marked advantages of the largest scale research activities over large and medium-sized ones.

(e) During 1945–9 there was no evidence in any of these industries of a systematic change in the effect of size of firm on the level of R & D expenditure, as related to sales volume.

SPECIAL SITUATION OF SMALL FIRMS

Small firms (with less than 200 employees) employ in total some two and a half million employees or one third of the manpower in British manufacturing industry, but they employ less than one sixth of the qualified scientists and what is more, while in all industry about 31 per cent of qualified scientists are employed in research and development, the figure drops to an optimistic 19 per cent for small firms.

Thus, proportionally the R & D effort of small firms is very much smaller than in large firms.

Usage varies, however, in small firms, as in industry generally and Table 2.9 shows the density of qualified scientists and engineers (QSEs) divided as to small firms and all firms in different industrial sectors. [20]

TABLE 2.9   DENSITY: QSE'S PER 100 EMPLOYEES

	Small firms	All firms
All manufacturing	0.7	1.4
Food, drink and tobacco	0.4	0.7
Chemicals and allied industries	2.2	5.2
Metal manufacture	0.6	1.4
Mechanical engineering	0.9	1.3
Electrical engineering	0.9	1.9
Electronics	5.8	4.4
Aircraft	1.9	3.0
Motor vehicles	0.5	0.7
Other vehicles	0.8	1.6
Textile, clothing, etc.	0.3	0.5
Other manufacturing	0.4	0.6

This confirms that in nearly all sectors of industry the density of QSEs in small firms is smaller than it is in the industrial sector generally. An exception is in the electronics industry where the ratio is actually higher in small firms. It is probably true that the technology of the electronics industry provides an exceptionally good environment for the employment of graduates in small businesses since it depends on progressive and advanced techniques which can be applied successfully in small premises with little capital. The same can sometimes occur in sections of the scientific instrument and pharmaceutical industries. However, the general picture remains that the ability to use scientific and technological personnel is linked with the capital intensiveness of an industry where the 'technological step' is expensive and out of the reach of small firms. Nevertheless the competition from large firms, and internationally, makes the position of small firms particularly vulnerable. There are many ways in which they can make use of R & D effort without spending a lot directly on it, as by the following means:

(a) R & D activities need to be considered carefully as an essential part of the policy of the firm. It is a good idea to have a co-ordinating committee (perhaps with outside R & D specialists present) whose job is to integrate all the R & D effort available and gear them to the requirements of the company.

The very undesirable antithesis to this is to have a small research department working on its own and only occasionally visited by someone from the sales department.

One of the first considerations of such a co-ordinating committee would be the advisability of the organisation having its own R & D department and its appropriate size.

(b) Careful consideration of the role of contract research facilities. Contract research can be carried out by contracting R & D people to work in the company or contracting a sponsored research institute (see p. 96) to carry out the work.

(c) Making an aggressive use of the appropriate research associations of which they should consider membership.

(d) Maintain the best possible contact with an appropriate university or polytechnic department.

(e) Attempting to associate themselves with the R & D of larger firms to whom they are suppliers.

(f) Greater use of consultants or part-time technical directors to bring to bear a wider impact of scientific knowledge to their operations.

(g) It is of course more economic in scientific effort to apply the results of research on a large production scale. A new development in a small firm will cost much the same as in a larger one but the cost will be recovered much more quickly if this discovery can be applied to a large production output. One way of dealing with this scale problem for small firms is to set up 'pooled' or 'subscription' research programmes, perhaps conducted by a research association, between a number of small firms with similar product intentions. [21]

Perhaps there is some comfort to be derived from the evidence that small firms expect to increase their employment of QSE's rather faster than for all firms. As against an expected increase from 1968–71 of 21 per cent for all firms a figure of 27 per cent for small firms has been recorded. [18]

INTERNAL v. EXTERNAL RESEARCH

An indication of how different industries behave in respect of internal research as compared to external expenditure on research is given in Table 2.10 where, for different industries, the external expenditure is expressed as a percentage of the total R & D expenditure.

Of this external expenditure, the larger firms again contribute the most (probably 70 per cent) but this represents a smaller proportion of their total expenditure than in the smaller firms (about 10 per cent). The figures in this table represent all external R & D expenditure by industry and not just that on co-operative research and it is difficult to conclude that co-operative research is in a satisfactory condition in this country for one would have thought that there are larger areas of common concern in industries than are represented by these figures – both in the sense of common needs in relation to immediate problems and a common interest in major furtherance of basic technologies in an industry.

TABLE 2.10   PERCENTAGE EXPENDITURE ON EXTERNAL R & D TO TOTAL
R & D EXPENDITURE (1966–67)

Food, drink and tobacco	6.9
Pharmaceuticals, plastics	3.2
Chemicals, petroleum products	3.5
Ferrous metals	6.5
Non-ferrous metals	10.9
Mechanical engineering	4.0
Scientific instruments	6.5
Electrical and electronic	1.1
Motor vehicles	3.5
Aerospace	0.03
Textiles, clothing	12.4
Miscellaneous	8.2

It is of relevance to note the view expressed in the Zuckerman Report, *The Management and Control of Research and Development* [22] (in Government Departments) that the first obligation on organisations controlling research, when planning their research projects is to ask 'Are they adequately informed on relevant research being done or planned in other Government Research Establishments, Universities, colleges of technology, industrial research associations and individual firms; and do they encourage organisations outside the Government either voluntarily or by extra-mural contracts to fill in gaps in the overall research effort relevant to their respective fields.'

In industry, except where it is nearly monopolistic, planning and conservation of scientific effort might be best achieved by having a much larger proportion of effort on a co-operative basis and with major expensive technological developments being planned on a central basis, making use of the effort available in various parts of the industry to fill the gaps in knowledge required by the central plan. Perhaps government should play a larger part than it does in sponsoring, encouraging and guiding such activities.

DATA FROM USA

It is interesting to compare these UK data with corresponding information from the USA – the most technologically advanced nation in the world – and to note factors of similarity and difference.

The same great increase in expenditure over the years is shown by Fig. 2.3 giving total expenditure figures from 1953 to 1973.

The relationship of R & D expenditure to the gross national product, affording a comparison, over time, of the relative importance with which R & D activities are rated in the economy, tells the same story of a peaking of activity around the mid-1960s, which we saw in the UK (Fig. 2.1) and now shown for the USA in Fig. 2.4. [83] In 1973 National Science Foundation figures give the expected percentage GNP figure as 2.4 compared with the peak figure of 3.0 in 1967 and further increase in the ratio over the 1972–3 level is not expected during the rest of the decade. (It will be noted that different sources calculate these ratios on somewhat different bases.)

In fact, as will be observed, the USA ratio is falling away quite sharply, while the UK figure is remaining almost constant.

EXPENDITURE BY DIFFERENT SECTORS

The total estimated spend for 1973 is the vast figure of 30,100 million dollars (about 12,500 million pounds sterling) or over ten times that spent in the UK. The breakdown of this into different sectors similar to that for the UK in Table 2.5, is given in Table 2.11.

TABLE 2.11   R & D SPEND IN THE USA ESTIMATED FOR 1973
(Dollars in millions)

	Carried out in each sector	Percentage	Finance supplied by each sector	Percentage
Federal Government	4,500	15.0	15,985	53.1
Industry	20,300	67.4	12,393	41.2
Universities and colleges	3,425	11.3	1,290	4.3
Associated FFRDCs	800	2.7	—	
Other non-profit institutions	1,075	3.6	432	1.4
Total	30,100	100	30,100	100

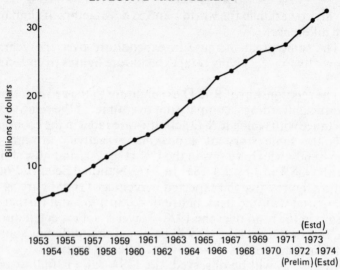

FIG 2.3 R & D funding trends in USA 1953–73

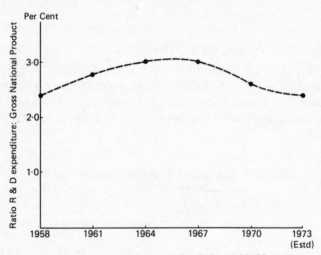

FIG. 2.4 Ratio R & D: GNP in USA 1958–73

Notes:

(1) FFRDCs or Federally Funded Research and Development Centres are organisations exclusively or substantially financed by the Federal Government to meet a particular re-

quirement, such as an atomic energy research programme or to provide major facilities for research and training purposes. They are frequently operated by universities (as indicated by the separate figures given here) or sometimes by private industry or non-profit making organisations (here included in the totals for each sector).

(2) Non-profit organisations include private philanthropic foundations which give grants to other sectors or public and private organisations that are involved in performing R & D such as non-profit sponsored research institutes.

It is immediately noticeable from these data that the proportion of funds provided by government is almost the same in both the US and the UK – 53.1 per cent in US, 51.7 per cent in UK.

But a much lower proportion is actually performed directly by government in the US – 15 per cent in US compared with about 30 per cent in UK (if public corporations and research associations are included). It follows that the US tends to contract out much more of its work both by the creation of FFRDCs, but much more by contract to private industry.

There is hardly any counterpart to the FFRDCs in the UK, although some of the stations funded by the research councils have some similarity in often being closely associated with a university.

There is no real parallel in the US with the research associations of the UK, perhaps reflecting the keenly competitive operations in industry in the US and a relative failure, therefore, to indulge in co-operative research for industry, or indeed for industry to be so dependent on government. Such trade associations as there are in USA are estimated to account for less than 1 per cent of the industrial R & D performance.

CIVILIAN INCREASE

As in the UK there is an increased emphasis on civilian priorities and away from defence and space related programmes, particularly in government funded operations. This is shown in Table 2.12. [83]

TABLE 2.12   TRENDS IN CIVILIAN R & D OUTLAY COMPARED WITH DEFENCE/SPACE

| Year | Total | Defence space outlays as % of total R & D | | Non-defence— non-space outlays as a % of total R & D | | |
		Defence related	Space related	Total	Non Federal	Federal
1953	48.3	47.5	0.8	51.7	47.0	4.7
1957	53.2	52.2	1.0	46.8	38.3	8.5
1961	54.7	49.2	5.5	45.3	36.3	9.0
1965	52.7	32.3	20.4	47.3	36.2	11.1
1969	44.6	33.5	11.1	55.4	43.0	12.4
1973	37.8	28.0	9.8	62.2	46.9	15.3

Among the programmes in the area of government financed civilian R & D are the development of health resources, air, water and ground transportation, educational improvement and research into energy resources.

UNIVERSITIES SPEND

As in the UK funds used for R & D in the universities and other colleges are growing much faster than the rest of the R & D budget. From 1953 to 1973 the universities R & D spend rose from $334M to $3,425M compared with the total USA R & D growth from $5,207M to $30,100M.

COST PER PROFESSIONAL SCIENTIST

Table 2.13 compares the cost per graduate in different research sectors for the USA for 1972. [83]

TABLE 2.13   COST PER FULL TIME EQUIVALENT SCIENTIST AND ENGINEER IN R & D

Sector	Number of FTE scientists and engineers	Total sector spend $m	$ per professional per year
Government	68,000	4,480	66,000
Industry	356,000	19,540	55,000
Universities	67,600	3,280	48,500
FFRDCs	11,800	769	65,000
Other	22,000	1,081	49,200

Within industry itself the cost per scientist in the 300 companies with the largest R & D programmes was $56,900, which was twice the cost in all the other R & D performing companies.

The trends, therefore, will be seen to be much the same: highly organised, development-oriented, sophisticated research costs more per professional. It is noticeable in this connection that industrial research in the US comes much nearer to government and indeed the disparities between different sections are not as great as in the UK.

The absolute cost of a professional scientist at about £25,000 is not so much higher in the US as might be expected when salary levels are taken into account, but no doubt multinational companies note the lower cost of employing scientists in the UK.

RESEARCH IN INDUSTRY

As we have seen from Table 2.10, in the USA over 67 per cent of all R & D, in terms of expenditure, is performed in private industry although only 41 per cent is funded by industry, the rest mainly coming from the Federal Government.

Table 2.14 shows how this expenditure is divided among different industrial sectors for 1972, (Column A) together with R & D expenditure as a percentage of net sales (Column C) and the number of FTE (full-time equivalent) scientists and engineers (Column B). Column D gives the ratio of scientists to total employment. All these figures are for 1971. [84]

The close parallel with the UK figures is clear. The aircraft and electrical equipment industries maintain a substantial lead: 81 per cent of all industrial R & D was performed by the leading five industries – aircraft, electrics, chemicals, machinery, motor vehicles. But apart from the fact that mechanical engineering is more highly R & D oriented in the US than the UK, nearly all industries, both high and low R & D performers, have much the same ratios of performance in each country and it is, perhaps, disappointing to note that in the US some of the smaller R & D performing industries are actually reporting decreases in their relative usage of scientists.

TABLE 2.14 RESEARCH & DEVELOPMENT CARRIED OUT WITHIN INDUSTRY IN THE USA 1971
(Dollars in millions)

	Total R & D funds	No. of scientists	R & D expenditure Net sales %	No. of scientists: Total employed %
Food, drink, tobacco	278	7,100	0.5	0.7
Chemical and allied products	1,766	41,400	3.7	4.0
Mineral oil refining	505	8,200	0.9	1.5
Primary metals and fabricated metal products	505	13,200	1.0	0.8
Mechanical engineering (inc. scientific instruments)	2,500	55,800	4.2	3.1
Electrical equipment and communication	4,523	87,700	7.3	3.8
Transportation and Ordnance (inc. aircraft)	6,699	102,200	7.7	4.3
	(Note: aircraft alone recorded a R & D funds/net sales ratio of 16.6% in 1971)			
Textiles, clothing, etc.	58	1,700	0.4	0.3
Wood, paper and printing	261	7,700	0.8	0.8
Rubber, leather, stone products	392	9,900	1.7	1.3
Miscellaneous (inc. business services)	675	15,124	0.4	3.7
Total	18,314	352,200	3.4	2.5

EFFECT OF SIZE OF FIRM IN THE US

In the US the four companies with the largest R & D programmes in 1971 accounted for 19 per cent of all industrial R & D, while the first 31 each spent over $100M, accounting for $11.2 billion or more than 60 per cent of all industrial R & D. Companies employing more than 5,000 employees account for 88 per cent of all R & D spend, although there are 10,742 R & D performing companies with less than 5,000 employees against 505 with more. Also the 100 companies with the largest R & D programmes while performing over 75 per cent of all industrial R & D accounted for 92 per cent of federal support.

We thus get a picture of even more concentrated industrial R & D into the largest firms in the USA than in the UK.

EXTERNAL RESEARCH IN THE US

Table 2.15 shows some figures [84] on the extent to which private industry contracts out its R & D to outside organisations.

TABLE 2.15   R & D CONTRACTED TO OUTSIDE ORGANISATIONS
BY INDUSTRY

Industry	Total R & D funds	Funds contracted to outside organisations	%
Food, etc.	278	7	2.5
Chemical and allied products	1,766	64	3.6
Mineral oil refining	505	6	1.2
Primary metals and fabricated metal	505	5	1.0
Mechanical engineering	2,500	17	0.7
Electrical equipment and communications	4,523	18	0.4
Total	18,314	331	1.8

It would appear that US industry is even more reluctant than the UK to go outside their own organisation to get part of their R & D carried out.

The overall comparison of breakdown of expenditure in the USA compared with the UK therefore tells us that the pattern of expenditure is much the same in the two countries except that the total expenditure is so much higher in the USA. There is a somewhat greater emphasis on government-aided co-operative research for industry in the UK and also a greater tendency for UK industry to go outside its own organisation for some of its research.

PROFITABILITY AND RESEARCH RATIO

The general impression given by data such as have been presented here is that research and development in industry inevitably produces an increase in profitability or at any rate avoids a decrease in profitability. The effects of science on the prosperity of science-based industry over many years can hardly be questioned but whether the profitability of firms in general is related to R & D expenditure is less easily decided. Very little work seems to have been done on this but one enquiry conducted by the Federation of British Industries (NIESR Report of 1962) concluded that if one picked out, in a given industry, those firms which had the greatest profitability between the years 1949–59, it would be shown that they were firms which employed a high ratio of scientists to other staff and conversely, firms which had the lowest profitability were shown to have a low 'research ratio'. No general correlation between profitability and research ratio for the firms in a given industry could, however, be demonstrated.

Of course, there are many factors which can be expected to influence the effect of research on profitability. One factor will undoubtedly be whether it is good research, soundly directed towards profitability aims both long term and short term, as distinct from the mere employment of graduates. Another will be the type of firm involved, for while it is convenient to group firms as being involved in generalised industry, such as the chemical industry, individual firms will differ widely in the effect that science, however well conducted, could have on their operation. A firm making sulphuric acid is likely to be less affected by science than a firm making insecticides because the changes are more rapid and fundamental in the technology of the latter and scientifically such a firm has to 'make more pace to stay in the race'. Also there are so many other factors affecting profitability, such as management efficiency, market stability, and sales ability that could nullify the effects of good science on the operations of a firm over a relatively short period. There is, therefore, no place for the complacent assumption that science means profits, and there does seem to be room for more scientific study of the economic effect of science in industry and indeed on other operations such as the effect of forensic science on crime detection, in order to elucidate the parameters which lead to research and development proving more 'profitable' in some circumstances. Such studies would probably have a much greater effect on industries now considered 'backward' in the use of science than the mere exhortation that they should use as much science as others.

One such study, carried out by the Science Policy Research Unit and known as the Sappho project (reported by the Centre for the Study of Industrial Innovation), has considered the factors which were found to be important in differentiating successful new products from failures and concluded that the important ones were:

(a) Successful innovating firms displayed a better grasp of user needs. The less successful ones tended to ignore user requirements and even user's views when offered.
(b) Successful innovating firms were better at marketing. The failed innovations were characterised by inadequate market research and neglect of publicity and user education.
(c) Successful innovating firms performed technical development more thoroughly than the less successful, though not necessarily more quickly. They tended to eliminate technical defects before launching on the market.
(d) The successful innovating firms made more use of outside scientific and technical advice and maintained more effective links with the scientific community in the technical area specific to the innovator.
(e) In successful firms the key managers involved in a new product had a higher rank and more authority than those responsible in the less successful firms.

While this study applies particularly to industrial research, the same considerations will undoubtedly apply to other mission-orientated research if 'marketability' and 'customer' relations' are suitable translated.

The advances that can be claimed by the application of science in the so-called 'science-based industries' are certainly enormous and there is reason to suppose that corresponding advances could be expected in all industries or other social activities.

THE CUSTOMER/CONTRACTOR RELATIONSHIP

In UK government circles, in particular, the principle has emerged forcefully in the last few years of organising the sponsorship of research in accordance with the so-called customer /contractor relationship. [82]

This principle implies that the department responsible in government for setting the broad objectives of the country is also responsible for seeing them attained. It follows that, where research and development are involved in their attainment, the department should also be responsible for defining their requirements in the clearest possible terms and for commissioning the R & D necessary to achieve them.

To do so successfully the departmental 'customers' must work in partnership with their R & D 'contractors' whether inside or outside the department. The responsibilities are then clear. Departments as 'customers' define their requirements: contractors advise on the feasibility of meeting them and undertake the work. Arrangements between them must be such as to ensure that the objectives remain attainable within reasonable cost.

This principle is obviously a sound one in theory. The danger arises from the necessity of putting over to the customer what R & D might be available to help him solve his problems, for viable research ideas are more likely than not to come from the research workers themselves.

It is, therefore, an essential feature of a successful application of the customer/contractor relationship that provision be made for continuing discussion and partnership between 'customers' and contractors and other interested and knowledgeable sections of the community.

Ideas for R & D must come from both sides and contractors must feel themselves free and encouraged to contribute towards the formulation of new research ideas.

The method of working should, therefore, allow the research contractor to put forward ideas for research programmes and demand of the department that sponsoring the ideas so put forward should be done with sympathy and understanding of the importance of novel ideas, so that some work is undertaken which, while being financed by the 'customer', is not immediately related to a specific objective and programme of work.

To take this even further it is essential that in all large social endeavours there should be a continuing activity of new basic research going on. Government undertakes this by continual support of the five Research Councils and the University Grants Committee, the purpose of this being to develop the sciences as such, to maintain a fundamental capacity for basic research and to support higher education.

The essence of the customer/contractor approach is the need for better discussions and partnership between all involved in these complex processes, whether in government or outside it, in utilising the research method towards the attainment of social goals. Such an approach should provide a partnership within which science will have more influence on the central policy of the 'customer' and contribute more directly and more effectively to making the best use of science and technology for the needs of the community as a whole.

The application of this principle should always be carefully considered in all its aspects whenever R & D is used to further the objectives of some 'parent authority' quite apart from government organisations, not forgetting that support of and contact with a base of original research is just as important as customer responsibility for sponsoring applied research programmes of direct and not so direct relevance to immediate programmes.

SUMMARY

Research and development can best be carried out with good knowledge of what is going on in research generally as well as in the particular field of one's research and this chapter is concerned with the background statistics of research in the United Kingdom and the U.S.A.

An attempt has been made to give a very broad picture of research and development activities on a national scale and in particular to show some of the trends of recent years. Summarising, we may say that total spending on science remains high in the UK and USA relative to other countries but appears to be stabilising in terms of GNP, with the government shifting its support substantially away from defence into civil fields while support for basic science as practised by the Research Councils is being curtailed slightly. Government continues to provide the majority of finance for R & D spending. Research Associations have not expanded in a manner which might have been hoped for.

Expenditure in different sectors – government, industry, the universities, etc. is discussed together with the changes that have recently taken place; university research is shown to be one of the most rapidly growing segments and the implications of this are discussed. Research in industry is discussed in some detail with different industrial sectors compared for expenditure, density of qualified scientists, percentage turnover, external expenditure on R & D, etc. Science-based activities such as aircraft, chemicals and electronics remain the greatest users although the more traditional are slowly improving.

The effect of size of firm and the particular position of the small firm are discussed with recommendations as to how small firms might deal with their science application problems. Similar expenditure data for the USA are given.

The relationship between profitability and research is discussed and studies described which consider the factors important in differentiating successful new product innovation from failures. Unfortunately the effects of science on profitability are insufficiently understood although there is some evidence that a high usage of scientists is likely to increase profitability, if well planned.

The customer/contractor principle which has emerged forcefully in the last few years, by which the customer is responsible for deciding what R & D shall be carried out, as well as paying for it, is a means of increasing the value of partnership between researchers and others involved in the complex processes of using research towards the attainment of sound goals. Treated with caution and with adequate facilities for basic research always to continue, this is seen as a healthy development.

3 The structure of R & D organisations

Research and development are carried out in many different situations, for different purposes, at different scales of magnitude and with different organisational structures, so that R & D departments are as variable as production activities, indeed probably more so, and nearly every such department is unique in the nature of its objectives, relations with parent organisations, structure and needs.

The tendency therefore in writing about the management or direction of R & D to assume that all such departments have sufficient of a common nature to justify generalisations about procedures must be resisted by both writer and reader. The assumption should be made that guide lines can be drawn which will command greater or less emphasis in one situation compared with another, rather than that they can and should be followed under all circumstances. The director himself is in the best position to know whether the activities of his department will be improved by the use of different techniques or arrangements.

In this chapter an attempt is made to consider the different types of Research and Development operations and some of the problems connected with them.

FROM LARGE GOVERNMENT LABORATORIES TO SMALL INDUSTRIAL LABORATORIES

The largest laboratories, such as the Atomic Energy Research Establishment at Harwell, the Royal Aircraft Establishment at Farnborough, the Atomic Weapons Establishment at Aldermaston and the National Physical Laboratory at Teddington would each have a total work force of many thousands with many hundreds of professional scientists, and such laboratories represent the peak of unified research and development organisation in terms of size and range of research activities. In the table below is given some information on the size of some of the larger government laboratories [23 and 24].

TABLE 3.1

	Professional staff numbers	Gross annual cost, including capital expenditure £m
National Physical Laboratory	700	6.9
National Engineering Laboratory	350	3.8
Warren Spring Laboratory	200	1.5
AERE Harwell	1200	16.4
AEA Winfrith	450	5.2
AEA Dounreay	300	13.5
AEA Risley	650	8.8
Computer-aided Design Centre	–	0.5

In these laboratories one might expect to find a high degree of sophistication in the research itself, the facilities employed, the formation and control of the research programme, the efficient supply and use of ancilliary services, the organisation and general administration. But even between and within these laboratories there will be a large degree of unevenness in the extent to which advanced techniques are used, often for very good reasons.

Of comparable size and sophistication are the laboratory complexes of large science-based industries. As laboratories scale down in size and change in purpose the problems which demand sophisticated attack in larger laboratories diminish or disappear so that advanced techniques for their direction are necessarily applied in simpler form, if at all.

Below the large laboratories in size, we reach a mid group, such as the larger research association laboratories, and many industrial laboratories. This is still a size where careful attention has to be paid to organisational structure and general administration.

Smaller laboratories such as the smaller research associations, the Research Council Stations and the majority of industrial laboratories represent a simpler problem from a management point of view.

A recent review of organisational structure for research and development in the pharmaceutical industry by the National Economic Development Office [25] concludes that there appear to be two breakpoints in the relation between size and structure. Beyond a total of about 300 total employees, close contact and therefore the need for minimal organisational structure tends to be lost. Between 300 and 1,000 employees a research centre can still be administered effectively with an appropriate organisational control. Above 1,000 employees, new problems of communication, co-ordination and control may tend to develop.

The larger establishments have great technical advantages which are often underestimated and which are considered later in this chapter, while establishments of lesser size have corresponding problems of trying to overcome their corresponding disadvantages.

PURPOSE OF LABORATORY

Another basic division between laboratories depends on their purpose. In some cases, as in the laboratories of private industry, the basic purpose can be expressed simply as being to maximise the profit, on a long-term basis, of the parent organisation. This is not simply a matter of carrying out research projects with a direct pay-off, it includes dealing with all those problems which might affect the image of the firm in its relationships with customers, government and the country as a whole. But in such circumstances the organisation is likely to be tightly controlled in budgeting and the choice of projects to have limited objectives in view.

Then there are the laboratories which provide a service such as the research associations supply to industry or the direct government laboratories supply to the community as a whole (see pp. 87–96). While the customer–contractor relationship is playing a growing part in all such laboratories, they inevitably have a wider purpose in developing a given technology or series of technologies and it is essential that they should have some freedom to so do. This needs to be reflected in their budgeting and organisational arrangements.

Even more concerned with social purpose are the laboratories connected with civil government departments, such as the Fire Research Station and the Water Pollution Research Laboratory of the Department of the Environment. In such cases it is desirable to maximise the impact of the research on the activities which it supports and the organisation needs to encourage the selection and planning of research programmes and facilities in relation to carefully chosen objectives, to conduct them efficiently and to supply services and control methods.

THE STRUCTURE OF R & D ORGANISATIONS

For whatever purpose a laboratory exists, if it consists of substantial numbers of scientists, mathematicians, engineers, technicians all of whom interact, it is necessary to pay attention to how they are organised so that the greatest creativity is reached as well as the greatest achievement of end product usage. The task is how to combine and group the talents of a number of technical men in the best way to improve communication, co-ordination, procedures and integration towards the true ends of the parent authority.

If one examines existing organisations – and successful ones at that – one finds a great variety of combinations. If one looks for simplicity in schemes of organisation, it will not be found. Nevertheless, certain patterns emerge about which valid comments can be made regarding their effectiveness for different purposes. Each actual organisation needs to examine itself continually against the significance of these patterns and purposes.

There are two basic aspects to examine. The first can be called the horizontal structure of the organisation or how the staff are grouped into unit blocks, interrelating side by side. The second deals with relationships between levels of authority in the organisation and the complexity of these interrelationships – the vertical structure of the organisation.

HORIZONTAL STRUCTURE

Certain different types of assembly of basic grouping occur with great frequency and may be regarded as the building blocks available to an organisation. [26] They are as follows:

(A) DISCIPLINE ORIENTATION

In this classical method of structuring an R & D department the department is divided into sections, each concerned with a particular academic discipline or subject, such as chemistry, physiology, or metallurgy. The subjects chosen will naturally depend on the problems predominant in the department. They may be quite limited, such as cryogenics, microbiology etc. Their particular feature is the tendency for everyone working in the particular discipline to be centred in the same division.

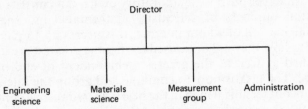

FIG. 3.1 Discipline-orientated structure

An example of this type of grouping is given by the National Physical Laboratory which has the structure shown in Fig. 3.1. Problems are either wholly solved within one of these groupings or a task is split up into a number of subtasks, each of which goes to a different group, or one group is the 'main contractor' for a task and it sub-contracts the parts more suitable to other groups.

The great advantage claimed for this structure is that centres of excellence can be built up in such a section, a more or less permanent team reacting between themselves in developing an appropriate expertise and developing real authority, however limited the field might be. Also career development is likely to be smoother and seem to be more fair, for management levels can be reached from within the section on a fair basis of performance. The management level personnel are likely to be of proven quality in the field and to have wide contacts in that field outside the organisation. It also avoids the duplication of expensive laboratory equipment and enables highly sophisticated and expensive equipment to be purchased and used efficiently. A man no longer required on one problem can be easily moved to another requiring a similar scientific background and to shift priorities between the different jobs in the group is easy without wrenching researchers away from their colleagues and superiors, thus giving a greater stability and security. The parallel between the discipline of a group and a subject area in the universities helps in attracting recruits and they feel more at home for the first years of their working life.

However, the pure discipline-oriented structure is only completely satisfactory if the tasks are as stated above and there is a tendency for the researcher to concentrate on the interesting scientific problems without reacting to the challenge of successfully producing a saleable end product.

PROJECT OR PRODUCT ORIENTATION

Where the overall objective of the laboratory is the practical one of developing products or processes and readying them for some 'market', the talents of men of a number of different disciplines are more likely to be needed – and to be associated with engineers, etc. An alternative then is for a project-orientated structure, where each group is performing a task within an overall organisation for pursuing a project.

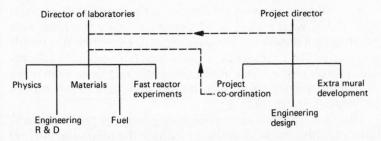

FIG. 3.2 Typical structure for fast reactor project R & D

A typical case is those laboratories of the Atomic Energy Authority which are concerned with developing the fast breeder reactor with most of their research directed towards answering problems concerned with the technology required to build a fast reactor. A simple expression of the corresponding organisational structure, which might be adopted is given in Fig. 3.2. It will be noted that in a large organisation of this sort the research aspects are to some extent organised on something similar to a discipline basis, though they are all orientated towards one product end-point.

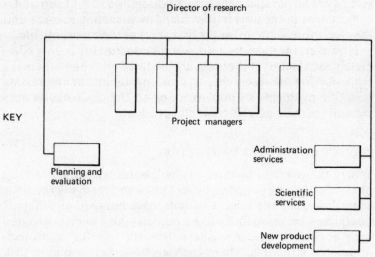

FIG. 3.3 Product or project-orientated structure

Also subject to project orientation is the organisation shown in Fig. 3.3, where an R & D department is concerned with developing a number of project ranges to be carried out simultaneously. The example here is the Beecham research laboratories where a recent reorganisation (1969) [25] has taken place to convert the structure into almost complete reliance on a project-based structure.

The advantages to be derived from project or product orientation are also many. It should facilitate the planning, evaluation control and costing of projects against both scientific and commercial criteria and it should give the individual research worker the challenge and stimulus of working in a wholly task-orientated environment. Unity of leadership towards the required product end-point is possible. It builds a reservoir of knowledge relevant to the problems of a particular type of product or project such as computational procedures, field behaviour of past products, or past defect problems. It provides a short linkage between research and 'engineering'.

In general it would appear from this that there would be a tendency towards the project-orientated structure for those organisations that were working towards the development end of the research spectrum, while in situations where the organisation was more likely to be dependent on research near to the basic end, discipline structure is likely to be used. For project-orientated structures do have disadvantages. Among these are the difficulty of cross-fertilisation of ideas of people of similar disciplines working on different projects. This makes it necessary for the researchers to try to be experts in many different skills and the experts to work in isolation. The mix of different disciplines within a project unit limits the opportunity of the unit head to rearrange assignments when projects change. The focus of project groups is on the development of endproducts: it becomes increasingly difficult for staff to withstand the pressures that arise and to find time for study and solution of long-term problems. Research of a fundamental nature will be neglected which dulls scientific creativity.

STAGE/PHASE STRUCTURE

In this structure, the more fundamental research, even though it be mission-orientated is separated from the development phase. This is not so much a different structure from the other two as a possible addition to or a modification of them. Much of the laboratory work will be exploratory and will not give a formula for prototype fabrication, but only where the research results are 'successful' and cost/benefit studies and market research is favourable, will the prototype stage be aimed at. The likely organisation chart in such a case, and a very common one, would be as shown in Fig. 3.4. But it would be highly desirable that there should be some flexibility about the composition of the prototype section so that some of the staff of the research division who had worked on the research before being taken to prototype phase should be on loan to the prototype section, as should some of the engineering staff who will be concerned with the further exploitation of the prototype if successful.

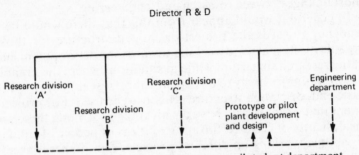

FIG. 3.4 Structure with separate prototype or pilot plant department

The advantage of this organisation is that it permits the scientist to continue working in his laboratory while the engineer is turning the ideas into prototypes or pilot plants. This recognises that some researchers are at their best at more basic research and find it more stimulating while others are more at home with development and coping with the practical problems appertaining thereto. The style of leadership also can afford to be different in the different stages, to the benefit of both.

MIXED STRUCTURES

Many situations can arise where the straightforward structural modes described above are undesirable. Indeed it is very seldom that a practical organisation does not consist of some modification.

Particular cases where modification is called for are, for instance:

(a) Where a laboratory might temporarily engage a major part of its research effort on a project, as for instance initiating a new manufacturing process, but after it is commissioned the laboratories might revert to departmental activities.

(b) Where the activities of a laboratory always combine a large amount of mission-oriented research with a certain number of projects also being pursued to marketability.

In all such cases it is likely that there will be a basis of discipline-based sections as a permanent part of the structure with some arrangements for linking them with a project organisation. In this way it can be hoped that the 'dynamic' project approach may be augmented by research mindedness and that a multi-discipline approach can be brought to bear on project development (Fig. 3.5).

There are many ways in which this linkage between discipline-based divisions and project activity might be accomplished. There may be a project section which provides project leaders who will temporarily draw off suitable staff from the research side or farm out tasks into the 'static' departments. There may more simply be project leaders appointed by and responsible to the director for each project task as it comes along. Or even less formally still, projects may be co-ordinated and controlled by project management committees. Committees are in any case likely to feature prominently in the strategic direction and planning of projects. The resultant structure might be as represented by Fig. 3.6. Where the problem of project operation always remains substantial and permanent, an organisation more like Fig. 3.5 may obtain.

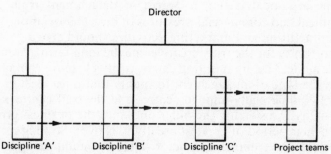

FIG. 3.5 Project teams formed by transfer from 'Discipline' Groups

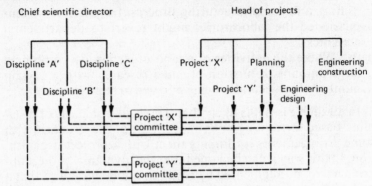

FIG. 3.6 Structure with permanent discipline and project organisations linked by committees

Retention of the discipline structure to some extent is usually justified by its many advantages. The term discipline should not be used in too narrow a sense, there being a tendency towards multi-discipline composition of all research divisions in recent times.

THE CENTRAL LABORATORY

In very large organisations, particularly industrial, a place has often been found for a central laboratory for the organisation as a whole, where basic mission-orientated work is carried out, with the business groups of the organisation carrying out project-oriented research and development work combined with commercial exploitation.

The argument is that a degree of detachment from the technical and commercial pressures of direct association with manufacturing and marketing activities should give a greater opportunity for the truly creative, maybe long-term advances to be made. The organisation can be relatively loose compared with the type of management formality that must exist in the more commercially-minded centres and the staff can be kept young by transferring the older ones into the business group after their period of greatest creativity is over. So long as the 'ivory tower' complex can be obviated by maintaining lively links with the business groups, as by temporary transfer of staff to project teams or even selling operations, this would seem to have many advantages.

Clearly there are many options available in the choice of R & D organisational structure. One has to ask firstly what does the organisation want of its research department – in the short term and in the long term? What kind of scientists, engineers and technicians are going to be needed? What part of the spectrum of research activities are they going to span? And what favourable conditions is it desirable to bring about? If one wants to encourage creativity, it is likely that cross-fertilisation of ideas will be aimed at. One would like to see the research staff familiar with and at least partially entwined with the achievement of goals. One wants smooth co-operation between all elements, the latest and best science brought to bear on any problem, the lowest expenditure and results in the right time. The structure has to be carefully thought out to achieve the objectives of the organisation concerned. No single pattern is right for all purposes.

VERTICAL STRUCTURE

COMPLEX ORGANISATIONS

While the broad division of activities may be made, horizontally, dependent on function, on the lines given above, the problem of the larger organisation in particular brings in greater problems of vertical planning. This is partly the problem of vertical communication between the laboratory, where the work takes place, and the establishment director, to ensure that the work done is in accordance with the needs of the parent authority, and that the parent authority can create policy in accordance with the results of the research effort; it is also partly the problem of ensuring that the greatest efficiency is exercised making the best use of the research workers. The usual reaction to this is to create a more complicated organisation in many directions, with various levels of control and many other structural arrangements.

The simple, purely flat hierarchy in which all the principal working scientists are at one level, responsible only to the research establishment director, is seldom maintainable for large organisations. The one man at the top cannot understand everything that is going on, communication upwards will be ineffective, co-ordination and conflict resolution becomes slower or is not carried out at all, and the aims of the establishment will not be met.

Before discussing the types of organisation met with in research establishments, however, it will be of use if we consider some of the recent studies that have been carried out on organisations, particularly in the United States.

THE NATURE OF ORGANISATIONS

Much has been written in recent years about the nature of organisations and how they are structured. It cannot be said that any consistent theory of organisations has yet emerged, but we do have a number of perspectives or conceptualisations that are becoming increasingly crystallised. [27]

Organisational arrangements are geared to the achievement of the goal of the organisation and are directed towards making the organisation more and more rational in the pursuit of this goal – more or less successfully. They are dynamic creations, however, subject to whatever pressures are exerted on them from outside and by those inside the organisation as they too are changed to meet changing goals. This is particularly exemplified in industrial research establishments where changing technology outside the firm forces the goals of the research department towards deeper scientific attack. This can result in a higher quality of scientists being brought into the organisation who, because of their different values, methods and expectations lead to changes within the organisation.

Katz and Kahn [28] typify organisations as

Production or economic	– providing the integration of the instruments of production achievement
Maintenance	– providing the integration of unchanging activities (churches, schools)
Adaptive	– providing the integration of expressive activities (research, art)

Managerial or political   – unions, pressure groups, etc. and look at organisational characteristics such as the distinction between instrumental and expressive orientations on the part of organisation members, i.e. whether they are motivated by receiving reward which will allow satisfaction to be sought outside or whether the members participate for some intrinsic satisfaction gained from their participation. These are clearly matters of degree, but a scientific establishment is likely to contain more members expressively orientated to a high degree and clearly fall into the category of 'adaptive'. Other typifications have also been suggested, including that of Pugh, Hickson and Hinings [29] who introduced the factors of:

Authority – an organisation can tend towards concentrated or dispersed authority.

Control   – an organisation can tend towards impersonal methods of control or towards live interaction.

Structure – varying between highly structural to lack of formal structuring.

In a research establishment there would be a tendency to dispersed authority, live control and an unstructured nature, but the pressures of size and complexity would inevitably lead to a degree of bureaucratisation towards the opposite extreme.

The characteristics of bureaucracy (an entity in social science and not an abusive term for over-organisation) are generally considered to be

Hierarchy of authority
Division of labour
Technically competent participants
Procedural devices for work situations
Rules governing behaviour of positional incumbents
Limited authority of office
Differential rewards by office.

Organisations primarily concerned with objects (even as 'people') will tend to be more bureaucratic than those concerned with ideas. There is therefore a basic conflict inherent in a large research establishment in the pressures to impose and withstand tendencies towards the 'bureaucratic' form of organisation. This is particularly so because of the power of specialists (scientists) who devise new procedures and control them, so making the concentration of authority and the imposition of rules from above difficult.

It is clear, however, that care is needed against over-simplification in the definition of organisation types, particularly to infer that certain organisation types are right for certain establishments (such as a certain size of research establishment) because the effects of goals, environmental factors, nature of staff and relationship with 'clients' among others will have marked effects.

We have noted that organisational arrangements are geared to the achievement of goals. Even if the goal is clear to the top executive, it may well be that the middle and lower echelons may have drastically different goals for the organisation and for themselves personally, and this will be particularly true of scientists with professional loyalties. Even in an organisation in which there is a high participation in decision-making and strong membership commitment, it is unlikely that there will be a totally unanimous consensus on what the organisation should attempt to do, let alone on the means of achieving these ends.

Goals are abstractions distilled from the desires of members and the pressures from the environment and internal system and always the goals of members, particularly high level ones, are crucial to what the actual goal is, however a higher authority may seek to establish it. This leads to the concept of an 'operative' goal as distinct from an official one and it is desirable that these should be as close together as possible because the allocation of major resources (money, personnel, equipment, etc.), a major factor in the achievement of final goals, will be determined by goal seeking at all levels of the organisation.

It is thus clear that effort should be made to get clearly expressed goals and to secure the co-operation of all levels of staff in meeting those goals as far as possible. But equally since goals will change it is incumbent on directors to be sensitive to changes in goal that are occurring. Changes can arise from

(a) direct interaction with relevant environmental factors – such as arise from competition, bargaining, coalition.

(b) pressure from internal sources as when new staff produce results powerful enough to make it profitable for the organisation to change direction.

(c) changed indirect environmental and technological demands – as when the original goal has been fulfilled, or when the technology level of the environment in which the organisation is working changes significantly. [30]

The effective achievement of goals must therefore be seen as a different thing from efficient working of an organisation. It is doubtful if an organisation can be effective with multiple goals.

Pugh [31] considers that organisations are likely to be more effective when they have a high degree of division of labour, specialised departmentalism, continuous systems of assembling output, the acceptance of the legitimacy of decision-making, a high degree of organisational autonomy and high rates of communication. In other words a disciplined approach to the structure and processes of the organisation with good communications throughout the organisation are likely to produce clear goals, clearly and effectively aimed at. The establishment of clear goals and the use of techniques for effectively (as well as efficiently) carrying them out is thus a task continually to be faced by the directors of an organisation.

THE STRUCTURE OF ORGANISATIONS

That organisations have structures, that large organisations generally have more complicated structures than small ones and that the complexity of structures and how they operate are associated with the number of major divisions (horizontal differentiation), the number of hierarchical levels (vertical differentiation), the number of different types of activities performed by the organisation, and the degree of co-ordination between them, are all self obvious. But what causes the structuring of organisations and what is the correct structure for a given set of activities are less obvious. Size itself for instance does not 'cause' the structuring of organisations, though large organisations do tend to have more functions performed by specialists who each build up their departments, more standardisation leading to further specialisation and more formal control of both operations and personnel and penalties for rule violation. Where large size is also accompanied by spatial dispersion, co-ordination also gives rise to the necessity of specialisation. Additional factors to size, however, also contribute to complexity of structure. More professionalism and higher levels of technology usually mean greater numbers of levels of hierarchy, because of increased communications needs as information is generated and utilised by the professionals for use by the larger organisations. But also, under these circumstances, the organisation tends to be more 'flat', i.e. there is not so great a differentiation between levels.

In a research and development organisation this tends to be taken to an extreme, so that a large number of hierarchical levels will be combined with a relatively flat structure simply because of the technological level and without relation to size absolutely. Comparison between a production department, therefore, and an R & D department's organisation would tend to be seen as shown in Fig. 3.7.

It can thus be argued that it is the decision to increase the number of activities or scale of operations, or changing to activities which require greater co-ordination, effort (all affected, if not effected, by external agencies), and the degree of technology involved as well as size, that effect the nature of the structure.

One aspect of the size and complexity of organisations is that large size both facilitates and has need of planning – a vital function in a changing society and in relation to the demands of public relations. So, for the top echelons of an organisation, control and co-ordinating power becomes less because the sub-units are large organisations themselves which have to be given considerable autonomy, but their power becomes more in terms of interaction with the environment and the creation of plans. Lower level personnel are thus still dependent upon those in higher positions, but on a different basis and the role of the elite becomes different rather than more powerful.

It also follows under these circumstances that the response to growth and complexity must be appropriate to the

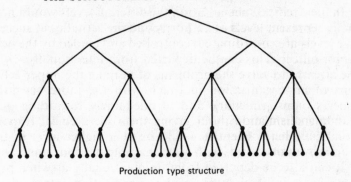

Production type structure

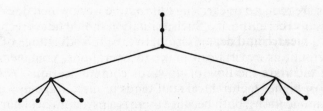

'Flat' research structure

FIG. 3.7 Structures according to communication needs

conditions under which growth occurs. The more that formalisation and co-ordination become the task of specialist subunits, the more must the new roles of planning and environment-reaction be built into the organisation at high level.

The complexity of organisations may be said to arise, as we have noted, from horizontal specialisation, vertical or hierarchical differentiation and spatial dispersion. There are many forms of horizontal specialisation, but they may be divided into task division and specialisation division. Task division is where an operation is broken down into sub-sections and organisational units set up to deal with sub-sections. Specialist division is where a particular function like training, maintenance, etc., is broken away from being carried out by everybody and centralised in a unit. Though in a research department horizontal differentiation is usually of the specialist type as we have seen earlier in this chapter, it can also have elements which are essentially task orientated.

In hierarchical specialisation the different levels would normally represent levels of authority and the activities at successive levels are co-ordinated, controlled and guided by the next senior officer. This can be departed from intentionally, as in the attempt to solve the problems of keeping the upper echelons of an organisation in touch with the more scientific aspects of project work and of adequately rewarding outstanding scientists without giving them hierarchical responsibilities. Such a scientist would be at a higher level in the hierarchy than accords with his management responsibilities.

It can also be departed from unintentionally as when perhaps because of changes in the organisation intermediate levels are reduced to carrying out routine work which does not carry any real authority. Such a situation should be corrected.

In a hierarchical organisation, to take full advantage of the contributions experts can make to operations, management must facilitate the flow of upwards communications. A low ratio of higher hierarchical staff tends to discourage upwards communications, both because there is a psychological barrier to communication against large hierarchical differences, and because too few higher echelons will mean that not enough time is available for communication to be effected. Indeed, where experts exist at all levels, as in an R & D department, hierarchical levels are not a matter of differentiating authority but of easing communications from bottom to top as well as top to bottom and arranging effort for planning and co-ordinating, internally and externally. The degree of external co-ordination necessary will depend on the relationship of the organisation with its environment, such as customers, production departments, government, etc.

Hierarchical organisations, therefore, are structured partly from their size, partly from the degree of technology involved in their activities and partly on the environment in which they work. Other factors which impinge include the underlying outlook and behaviour of their members (thus civil service research organisations will tend to have more hierarchical levels than industrial) and the traditions and idiosyncracies of individual organisations. The latter can be particularly important when changing from a less to a higher technological level of activities, with the potential for damage because tradition will not easily accept the greater number of hierarchical levels required. [31, 32]

One other concept of value in analysing complex organisations is that of integration (Lawrence and Larsch) – 'the quality of the state of collaboration that exists among departments that are required to achieve unity of effort by the demands of the environment' [33] Organisations are more effective when they meet environmental pressures and when they allow their members to achieve their individual goals. There is some evidence that a degree of conflict between departments and levels is not a bad thing for effectiveness (see p. 237), but integrating or conflict-resolving agencies are necessary if goals are to be achieved. In times of technological change these integrating agencies need to operate at many levels and not only at the top.

Thus we see that complex organisations are indeed complex in many ways. They grow or diminish in size and complexity to meet the demands placed on them as a consequence of their relationship to higher authority, to external environments, to internal pressure, and to changes of goals. They are continuously dynamic, more at some times than others. They exist to meet their aims which are themselves complex and to satisfy the aspirations of their members. They are centres of conflict and conflict resolution.

The director of a research establishment needs to be aware of the creature that he has under his nominal control and to adjust the structure and processes of his organisation continuously.

HIERARCHICAL STRUCTURE IN RESEARCH ESTABLISHMENTS

In the hierarchical structure, as the activities at successive levels are co-ordinated, controlled and guided by the next senior officer, in practice it will be found that there is a strong tendency for fairly autonomous groupings to be at much the same size as correspond to the breakpoints suggested by the NEDO report quoted above. Divisions of 200–300 total staff are formed under a divisional director with assemblies of three or four of such divisions forming groups under a director with a certain larger autonomy. A number of such group heads might serve the director of a particularly large establishment, but in such a case the structure will also become complicated by the specialised functions that have to be introduced.

In Fig. 3.1 was shown a simplified discipline-orientated structure. Fig. 3.8 shows a similar structure but drawn with the typical layers of a vertical structure.

An organisational structure by itself is not, of course, enough to make an organisation function and where the efforts of a number of sections have to be integrated, a network of inter-group committees is likely to be also found. This will be discussed later.

As successively higher levels of staff move further away from the actual conduct of research, their ability to understand it becomes less, and their ability to direct the research itself, in any way, becomes minimal. The job of levels senior to the level above the principal working scientist level becomes a matter of providing the right means and environment, guiding the general direction of the ends of the research work and controlling the resources available, communicating by absorbing the nature of the research work done and using this knowledge to help create the best policy for the next senior level, while absorbing from the higher level the purposes of the parent organisation and translating them into terms of project selection, and termination.

Although necessary to large research stations, nevertheless such an organisation pays a penalty not shared by the smaller establishment in which a limited number of principal working scientists are only answerable to the director. In such a case if the department is small enough, real direction and full understanding of the research work can be undertaken by the director who is himself the point of contact with the parent authority. A good director, with good principal scientists, is more likely to produce original research ideas of exploitable value under these circumstances.

It remains, therefore, a considerable problem for the large, vertically organised, particularly project-based organisation to maintain the organisation needed for projects but at the

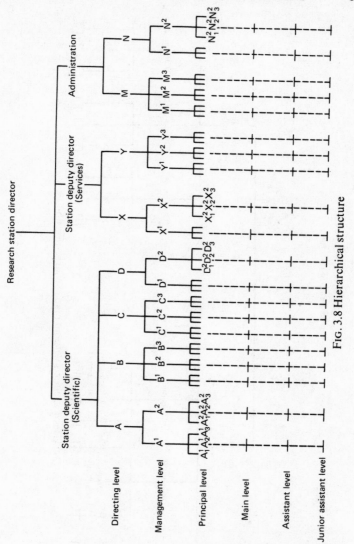

Fig. 3.8 Hierarchical structure

same time to operate on the principle of the small, good team with a director adequately in touch with the higher managements' objectives. One partial solution to this problem has been to appoint outstanding scientists to posts at various levels

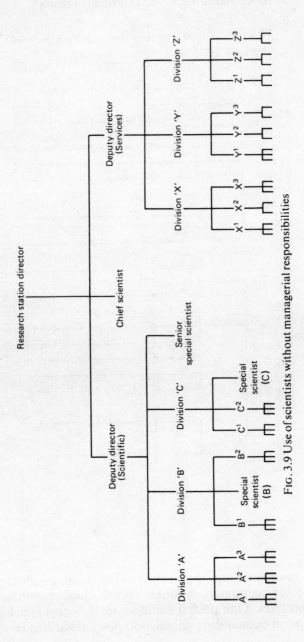

FIG. 3.9 Use of scientists without managerial responsibilities

in the organisation, but without the usual responsibilities associated with direction of large scientific 'empires' and therefore working with a small team forming a cell of scientific excellence with high level contacts, or being allowed to roam at will over the problems of his department (see p. 66).

The organisation chart might then become modified to that shown in Fig. 3.9.

While such scientists are likely to perform some tasks which contribute to a project, they are more likely to be used on background 'strategic' research and thus to throw up ideas which the research management can exploit by incorporation into the project strategy or to form the basis of a new project.

Equally for the laboratory organised on a horizontal pattern, as it gets larger and the desirability of operating multidisciplinary research projects of a large strategic pattern grows, organisational problems will lead towards complex organisation, although this may well meet with the antipathy of scientists used to working on their own in isolated cells. This is an example of the interplay of internal and external forces in the development of organisational structure.

Since modern research tends towards multidisciplinary, large-scale projects that are mission-orientated – whether building a fast reactor or finding a cure for cancer – the type of organisation is of considerable importance and deserves closer specific study than has so far been given.

ORGANISATIONAL PROBLEMS RELATED TO INVENTION AND INNOVATION

There is a fundamental organisational dilemma in R & D organisations that the organisational conditions for inventive success may be quite opposite to those promoting successful innovation. In other words the organisational features which increase the probability that a firm, for instance, will stimulate the production of new ideas may be precisely those factors which decrease the probability that the ideas will reach an implementation stage.

Wilson [34] argues that a 'diverse' organisation (in terms of having a number of specialist technical and staff groups and in having activities which are varied, unprogrammed, not closely defined or budgeted) is more likely to produce 'inventive' ideas. Support for this lies in the writings of many authors. Thus Knight [35] concludes that creative people are of the sort who work happiest in a 'diverse' organisation, and Hage and Aiken [36] conclude that employees with specialist training and belonging to professional bodies, with wide external contacts, are more likely to yield new ideas. Moreover an organisation with a number of specialist groups appears to be conducive, by processes of rivalry and intercommunication to be productive of new ideas.

On the other hand Wilson argues that 'the greater the diversity of the organisation, the smaller the proportion of major innovative proposals will be adopted'. This is because the process of adopting and implementing new proposals is firstly a political one, and with a diverse organisation a new proposal is likely to provoke resistance, counter proposals, and difficulty in reaching a firm implementation decision. This is also a reason why a large company often finds it more difficult to adapt to innovative changes – because it is decentralised, with powerful sub-groups, and agreement to adopt proposals is more difficult to secure.

Indeed this characteristic of a large company, together with emphasis on routine and departmentalism to which large organisations drift, is also not conducive to the creation of new ideas. It is, therefore, supportive of the idea (p. 30) that as firms grow larger there is a curvilinear relationship between size and innovation, the really large firms not getting the economies in scale as fully as might be expected.

Clearly, between inventive and innovative activities, two different types of organisational pattern should exist with the very strong need for a degree of liaison between them and devices for integration. The project team type of organisation is a particular and far-reaching integrative device where those who have been concerned with idea creation join with the team concerned with development and implementation on what might be a full-time or consulting basis, but at the end of the project return to their more 'diverse' research organisation.

There are, of course, great differences in the type of innovation that is being aimed at. The more that it is concerned with uncertain, unpredictable and complex developments the more the appropriate organisation is to reform traditional functional divisions (or parts of them) into networks of specialist elements. Certainly an organisation which serves to erect barriers between research activities and other operations essential to successful innovation would make it difficult to implement successful innovation.

SIZE OF RESEARCH ESTABLISHMENT v. EFFECTIVENESS

In Chapter 2 comments have been made about the particular problems of small firms in relation to research activities and these remarks may be considered to apply to any small research effort in relation to a small enterprise. A description has also been given of studies on the effect of size in industrial firms on research effectiveness. In this chapter we have also considered some of the effects of size as reflected in organisational problems.

However, perhaps the greatest importance of size lies in the comparison between large research organisations and small ones so far as their research effectiveness is concerned. This would be very difficult to study in a purely academic fashion because as we have seen, research establishments tend to be the size they are because of the function they are performing, and research establishments exist for so many different purposes that they cannot easily be studied for a single parameter.

It cannot be denied, however, that large multi-disciplinary research establishments are superlative organisations for producing technological advance on a mammoth scale, from basic research through to advanced pilot-scale development. Nuclear energy achievements on both civil and military sides are ample evidence of that. It is very doubtful if achievements of this magnitude could be made without such establishments.

The advantages they offer include:

1. The existence of stations of acknowledged excellence attract the most capable of scientists.
2. Because so many good scientists of all types of discipline that may be relevant to the problems are closely associated, they, with all their good contacts, will always be able to tap

available knowledge to give a lead in mission-orientated research, and to isolate areas which must be attacked by new research.

3. The existence of an atmosphere of good scientific achievement challenges all the scientific workers to improve their ability and widens their experience to make them more effective.

4. The multiple-level hierarchy organisation conveys a degree of eminence to the more senior staff which gives them effective entry to most resources, externally, that are required.

5. The more expensive and sophisticated equipment can be used for much of its time because of the large population which wishes to make use of it directly or indirectly and it becomes, therefore, relatively low in cost.

6. This also applies to direct services, such as engineering and information which can be established and operated with specially skilled staff, and modern, plentiful equipment to provide well-organised and efficient services.

7. Because services are on a large scale, they can face the design and installation of large and very costly development stage projects with sound control over any contractors they find necessary. Indeed they advance the technology of most contractors with whom they are involved.

8. Large, skilled and efficient contract and finance organisations can also be established which make for smooth arrangements suitable for the purpose in question without taking up too much of the scientist's time.

9. Each scientist therefore has enormous resources available to him and if he learns to use them effectively he can achieve much more in depth and magnitude than if he were in a small laboratory.

10. The planning of whole, large projects can be carried out by professionals skilled in planning, and such planning, integrated with the management chain, can ensure that every aspect of research work is aligned, as required, with the eventual result.

11. Economies of scale can also be exercised in purchasing, routine engineering services, efficient use of labour, computer-aided administration, etc.

These advantages would be less obvious in research organisations which existed for a multiplicity of purposes rather than having one main technological aim, but many of the advantages would remain, particularly those related to the greater scientific achievement, as shown by the success of the UKAEA laboratories in their diversification activities.

Evidence could, therefore, be justifiably advanced for some degree of amalgamation of smaller laboratories in a way which would convey the benefits of larger scale operation. We shall see in Chapter 4 how accumulations of small laboratories tend to cluster in certain university areas and how there has been a good deal of merging of industrial research associations in recent years. These situations could well be re-examined from the point of view of further direct association to produce complexes with larger identities.

Attention should, however, also be paid to the advantages of small laboratories which are in many ways more suitable to some types of scientist who do not like the constraints imposed of necessity by large organisations, who are not mentally equipped to utilise great resources, whose freedom itself is important to them as an environment for creative ideas. Research management should continually be seeking to allow free expression of scientists within the confining influences of large organisations.

RELATION BETWEEN RESEARCH AND DESIGN

The more obvious cases of the impingement of research and design on each other is where physical or chemical research is conducted in order to arrive at a prototype engineering machine or a pilot-plant for carrying out chemical or physical reaction. Much the same interrelationship occurs, however, wherever research is project orientated. A new strain of wheat has to be 'designed' in terms of a statement of how it can be obtained in a form which is practicable for the market and copyable. A medical treatment has to be 'designed' so that it is reproducible, applicable at a reasonable cost and has taken into account side effects and the variable nature of patients. So much the same principles are likely to apply in all such cases.

The relationship is, however, frequently not acknowledged and frequently causes organisational problems. One of the reasons for this is that in R & D organisations with a functional or discipline basis the designer may well be in an entirely separate branch of the organisational tree to that of the research scientist. (In medical research it is likely that the man who brings the research to the point of reproducible application will not even be in the same organisation as the research being carried out.)

There then arises a tendency for the scientist to consider his work finished when he has established a new principle and for the engineer to wish to design his prototype without waiting for the research to be finished. Alternatively, the scientist tends to pursue his research in more and more detail, making the task of incorporating fresh ideas into the prototype by a reasonable time impossible.

For successful project-orientated research a much more sophisticated association is necessary and the contribution of the designer needs to be acknowledged from the early stages of a project by the scientists and vice versa. After a research project begins to look successful, scientifically, and in accordance with market criteria, it is time for the designer to become associated with it. He will formulate some of the preliminary design concepts but should avoid going into detail. This will begin to give a pointer to the areas of technology that still need to be explored before a design can be achieved and this will give guidance to the research plan to be followed from then on, which may well effect a change in the original strategy. On the other hand the preliminary design may throw up areas of ignorance which it would be very expensive or impossible adequately to explore and in such a case doubt may be justifiably thrown on the project and lead to abandonment or to a new design concept being investigated requiring an easier technology. The final prototype design will thus be arrived at after a series of dialogues between researcher and engineer, and when it is built it is more likely to accord with the principles the research has indicated, to have minimised the total research expenditure necessary and to yield a product suitable to the particular 'market' it is aimed at.

To carry out such an intricate association of researcher and engineer, however, demands attention to the organisation. A monolithic and separate engineering organisation only responsible to the establishment director might well be viewed with suspicion, although there are considerable advantages in engineers belonging to an engineering division – advantages of developing high standards of engineering, common engineering standardisation, and career development of engineers. One helpful move is to appoint a project leader with understanding and experience of engineering, if he be a scientist, or of research if he be an engineer, and another is to post engineers to scientific divisions to work directly with scientists at an appropriate point in a research project. There is, however, always a need for continuous awareness of and education in the absolute necessity of the 'design' function being complementary to the research function, wherever research is expected to lead to an application.

RELATION BETWEEN INTERNAL AND EXTERNAL RESEARCH

We have seen in Chapter 2 that Government spends more than half its research expenditure outside its own establishments (Table 2.6) but that industry (Table 2.8) spends relatively little, with the 'traditional' industries (textiles, non-ferrous metals) spending a higher percentage than the science-based industries.

There appears to be a natural tendency for research workers to want to carry out their research entirely by themselves, heedless of whether similar work is being done elsewhere, whether they have the best facilities for the work, or whether they have the best background knowledge for the work. Certainly full understanding of any field is only obtained by working in it, but project-orientated research becomes more and more dependent on a multifarious range of research disciplines and even basic research becomes more dependent on a range of disciplines being brought to bear on larger problems, so that one has carefully to question the wisdom of keeping one's research to one's own laboratories. It has certainly been noticeable in the last few years that more and more research is being 'bought-out' and 'contracted in' in the major research establishments and more and more specialist 'sponsored' research and consultant establishments of various sorts have arisen. Since research becomes more highly specialised and demands ever more expensive equipment, it should be more economic to use those skills and that equipment continuously where it is available, rather than have research workers continually learn entirely new skills or allow expensive facilities to be duplicated in many laboratories and then stand idle for most of its time. Again, work in a certain specialised field may only be wanted for a short time, so that it would be uneconomic in time and money to build up a new laboratory with new staff and facilities that could only be dispersed at the end of the work, when another organisation exists which already has facilities and staff available which could undertake the required work.

So one of the important considerations of any research director should today be whether he is achieving the correct balance of work within and without his own laboratories. He will obtain the maximum advances by spending some money on sponsored research, some on co-operative research, some on university contracts and at the same time always considering the potential for selling research outside, where he has facilities and specialised staff temporarily not engaged on work of the highest productive advantage. To this latter end the costs of the expensive equipment they use should always be apparent in the cost control of research divisions, for to make equivalent scientific advances nowadays requires much more expensive equipment than hitherto, particularly in 'big' science such as nuclear physics and radio-astronomy.

In seeking to establish the best sources of research information, it is nowadays most important to consider international collaboration both in the sense of buying knowledge, and so avoiding the conduct of research to rediscover it, and paying for research to be carried out where an overseas organisation is particularly skilled in a required field.

Indeed many large industrial firms now operate on a basis of doing hardly any research themselves but licensing knowledge or sponsoring research on a wide international basis.

The present position therefore is that research is very much in the market place for both buying and selling, and a director of a research team needs to weigh up very carefully what product in the form of knowledge and research activities he can buy or sell, to keep his own research activity functioning at a maximum of scientific impact with a minimum of outgoing cost.

It is clear that the organisation of research and development can be instituted in many forms – in functions and purposes, in structural organisation and in size.

The director of any unit needs to have some awareness of the options open to him and of the considerations that come into play in the operation of organisations. He will, at the same time, be aware that his own organisation, dependent as it is on the individuals that make up the team and the curious diversity that enters into the work pattern of his unit, is unlikely to be helpfully squeezed into any particular academic pattern. It remains for him to seek out and judge the final pattern that suits his own conditions best, remembering that an organisation cannot simply be imposed, that it has an identity which can be affected in many ways by the forces inside and surrounding it.

SUMMARY

That research and development are carried out in so many situations as to make over-generalities undesirable must be recognised. Laboratories vary in size (statistics for the large government laboratories are quoted) and sophistication in social purpose and in relation to their projected endproducts. The structure of R & D organisations is discussed in relation to horizontal and vertical organisation.

Horizontal organisations have their variations in relation to discipline orientation, product or project orientation, mixed organisation, stage phase organisation, the central laboratory, with many devices to make the best of the advantages and minimise the disadvantages of each type, which are discussed.

Vertical organisations are considered in relation to theoretical ideas on complex organisations. Many aspects of comparison between the bureaucratic and organic basic types of organisation with particular reference to their application to R

& D are made and discussion held of the role of goal definition and the effect of internal and external forces on this. The changing roles of higher echelons of organisation are considered as is the place of the special scientist at high echelon level. The fundamental dilemma of organisations suitable to inventive success not being correct for promoting successful innovation is also discussed.

The advantages of size in research establishments – the economy of scale and how further use might be made of this by associating laboratories on a more formal basis – are dealt with, as is the interplay of research with design of end product and the relation between research carried out internally and externally to an organisation.

Choosing the right organisation for any R & D effort is full of complications but only by being aware of the factors involved can the final pattern be chosen which suits individual conditions best.

4 Available sources of research effort

A short account will now be given of the general ways in which research is carried out in the UK, paying particular attention to the use that can be made of the different resources by research departments in industry or elsewhere.

UNIVERSITIES AND POLYTECHNICS

In Britain, as in all countries, the majority of fundamental scientific work is carried out either at or in association with the universities or the polytechnics. The essential atmosphere of fundamental science is that the experimentation and scientific thinking are done purely for their own sakes and without reference to value to the community in a direct sense, to the requirements of industry, the government, or anyone else. It is important that this should be so because it is seldom that one can forsee the future applications of research and certainly none of the more notable breakthroughs in knowledge such as concern electrical energy, atomic energy, organic dyes and radio-waves would have been made if a highly probable return on the money they cost were a prerequisite of its being spent. This, however, would be a reasonable expectation of most research outside universities, although the return expected may not in itself be economically based.

The desirability of association of research establishments with universities has already been mentioned in Chapter 2, where it was stated that one of the ways of effecting such an association was for the research establishment to sponsor research contracts with the university on subjects of mutual interest. Such subjects have to be chosen carefully, so as not to raise the fear in the university that their own research activities should be weakened, to provide a suitable basis for academic research which can lead to the award of higher degrees and not such that in general the results are important on a fixed time scale for some project end point of the research establishment.

There are, however, other ways also in which association between universities and research establishments can be fostered. [37] Firstly, it is possible to encourage closer staff relationships by giving selected members of the staff of research establishments university status, and involving them in giving short courses of lectures in their field of research or helping in the supervision of research students, or taking part in the discussion of university policy on research and advanced teaching.

This type of association is particularly practised by staff of some of the research units of the Agricultural Research Council and Medical Research Council, but has in recent years been growing to a significant extent even with industrial research laboratories.

Secondly, it is possible to conduct co-operative research projects between a research establishment and a university, particularly in fields in which the establishment has a strong technological interest but where basic scientific understanding is meagre and where highly specialised and expensive equipment which can be used for underlying research is available at the research establishment.

Again, positive association between research establishments and universities is possible even to the extent, as frequently happens in the USA and to a certain extent in continental countries, of the university having responsibility for or a close association with the operation of the establishment either fully or in part. In the UK this is practised, for instance, between the University of Birmingham and RRE Malvern. It may be argued, however, that a research establishment's job is mainly technological research, mission orientated, whereas the university's is to provide background research and that such positive association could be harmful to both unless confined to those activities of a research establishment related to background research. An improvement in association is obtained by the recognition of some work in research establishments for the conferment of higher degrees, particularly PhD. This has the advantage that university supervisors of the research would become associated with the work of the establishment and known to the staff. Whether, however, the conferment of PhD is so highly regarded or useful as to justify the considerable changes in most universities' rules must be of some doubt, while a note of injustice appears in the research establishment if one man happens to be put on work which can earn him a PhD while another of equal merit is forced by the requirements of the establishment's programme to do work which could not be so rewarded.

A greater mobility of university supervisors into research establishments (and of establishment staff into universities) does, however, seem very desirable for improving the association of research arrangements, and administrative problems which mitigate against such moves are receiving serious consideration.

The association of a research establishment with universities is related to the formation of an infrastructure of scientific knowledge upon which the establishment staff can rely for greater understanding of the technology it is pursuing, the easier to formulate fruitful programmes either for the improvement of existing processes or for taking the next steps towards innovation. It is also related to the recruitment of scientific staff to the research establishment already orientated towards the work of the establishment and partly trained in some of its techniques. It is to be expected that this type of association will be very much further developed as directors of research are pressed to make more use of external specialised effort on economic grounds and to take even greater care in creating an environment where sound topics for fruitful development can be imaginatively conceived.

Over the past few years there have been established inside universities units which provide an interface between the research workers and industry or other technological enterprises. These liaison units vary considerably in size and method of operation – from Strathclyde's Centre of Industrial Innovation to a single individual liaison officer – and their financial support is derived from a number of sources. They do, however, have the common aim of speeding the transfer of scientific knowledge from the universities to industry and to improve liaison generally between the two sides.

Appendix 4.1 (see end of chapter) gives a list of research institutes, establishments and units and these are shown mapped in Fig. 4.1 in relation to universities. It will be seen that there is already a significant grouping of such establishments, close to universities. [37]

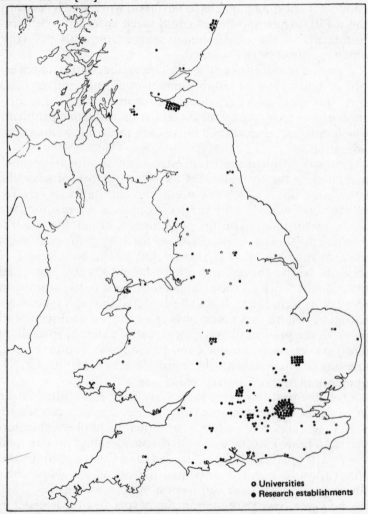

FIG. 4.1 Map showing universities and research establishments in the United Kingdom [37]

An even closer association is perhaps foreshadowed by the building of a new laboratory for Messrs Tate and Lyle on the campus of Reading University (1972).

GOVERNMENT DEPARTMENTS

Perhaps the closest approach to fundamental scientific work outside the universities is to be found in government departments (including the Atomic Energy Authority). As we have seen, such work accounts for the largest single expenditure on research and development in the country, particularly in the defence field where basic research is necessary because the needs of defence are of such a nature in the twentieth century that it is possible to keep in the race at all only by exploring most likely scientific avenues. The effect on industry of this effort is twofold. Firstly as we have noted, government research contracts involve a higher expenditure than direct government research. The work that is put out to industry under this heading is usually development of the ideas basically worked out by the government research establishments. Industries which are in contact with government laboratories in this way not only, therefore, put themselves in a commanding position for production contracts when development ideas are successful but, what is more important from the point of view of the relationship between science and industry, they put themselves in contact with the largest body of scientific research in the country, which will inevitably affect their development in civilian fields. The outstanding and obvious example of this, of course, is the aircraft industry where undoubtedly the interest of governments in aircraft for defence purposes has been almost the sole factor in the immense strides taken during the last twenty years in civilian, commercial aircraft.

Undoubtedly the money spent by the government on defence since 1940 has produced tremendous secondary effects on industrial developments in this country. It is a matter of conjecture whether without the war the same expansion of scientific application to civilian industry would have occurred, but certainly it would be a tempting exercise to speculate on what might have happened if all this research effort had been put directly into civilian industry on a broadly planned basis.

For of course the only industries which can benefit from science through government laboratory contracts and through contracts directly are those which are working in a field relevant to the requirements of the departments in some way.

TECHNICAL SPIN-OFF FROM ADVANCED R & D

The effect of the existence of the advanced technologies in government departments, such as the Atomic Energy Authority is difficult to gauge although it is inevitable that technological advances will arise, which could benefit a wide range of other technological activities such as industry.

There are two types of such 'spin-off' as it is called. The first is direct, and examples of this may be taken from the nuclear energy field as follows:

(1) Application and use of isotopes and high energy radiation in such fields as medicine, sterilisation, radiation instrumentation and materials alteration and ion implementation for doping of semiconductors.

(2) Heat transfer – where advances occurring in relation to the design of nuclear reactors and process plants are being supplied to industrial processes including desalination plants.

(3) Analysis – such as the new microwave spectrometer for the rapid analysis of complex, involatile substances.

(4) Cryogenics – studies of the properties of He_3 and He_4 produced a new principle of refrigeration leading to commercial refrigerators for very low temperatures ($0.015 - 0.020°K$).

Positive efforts are being made nowadays in many directions to ensure that such new technology is applied elsewhere, and the NRDC (see p. 98) exists partially to assist in the flow and use of it.

The second is the indirect, intangible spin-off which arises from the existence of advanced technology as it comes into contact with other lower technology activities and gradually improves them. It acquaints those in contact with the advantages of more powerful thinking and gives them confidence that difficult scientific and engineering concepts can be subdued to practical ends. Extraordinary knowledge of materials, of physical fields, such as areas of high Reynolds number, or of environments such as clean air, parade new platforms for the take-off of advances in fields not directly concerned. Probably this second spin-off is the more important for it is of a nature that would be unlikely to take place if research were not undertaken in entirely new fields of major challenge. [38]

GOVERNMENT LABORATORIES

The laboratories which the government supports directly or through some council, authority or other public body fall into four groups:

(a) Defence laboratories.
(b) Laboratories directly controlled by the Department of Trade and Industry, the Home Office or the Department of the Environment, etc.
(c) Laboratories sponsored by the Department of Education and Science working through the Science Research Council system.
(d) Laboratories of the public corporations.

DEFENCE LABORATORIES

As the name implies these laboratories are concerned with supporting the operations of the Ministry of Defence. They are still organised into three categories reflecting previous association with the Navy, Army and Air Force, although attempts are presently being made at some rationalisation. While, naturally, much of their activity is security controlled, nevertheless they maintain wide networks of communication through sponsoring work in universities, industry, etc., much of which is not so controlled and they publish widely the results of their work where conditions are appropriate. They are also increasingly willing to accept contract work where their special facilities or skills can aid the sponsoring body.

The main laboratories in this group are:

Royal Aircraft Establishment, Farnborough
Explosives Research and Development Establishment, Waltham Abbey
Royal Radar Establishment
Royal Armament R & D Establishment, Fort Halstead
Admiralty Materials Laboratory, Holton Heath
Central Dockyard Laboratory
Signals Research and Development Establishment
Natural Gas Turbine Establishment
Rocket Propulsion Establishment
Atomic Weapons Research Establishment, Aldermaston (transferred from the UKAEA in 1973)

LABORATORIES DIRECTLY CONTROLLED BY OTHER DEPARTMENTS OF STATE

These laboratories cover a wide range of activities. Their functions have been summarised as follows:

(a) to keep their fields of research under constant review in order to define objectives and to help the Government, industry and public to maintain a lively interest in the value of research;

(b) to conduct research which can provide information to central and local government on matters such as air/water pollution, road safety, noise and the extinction and prevention of fires, in which the Government has a clear responsibility for protecting the health, safety and welfare of the citizen;

(c) to carry out research and development in subjects, such as the design and construction of buildings and roads which are important to the Government and which affect the efficiency of industry as a whole;

(d) to extend the frontiers of knowledge in applied science so that industry can be provided with the basic information required for the solution of particular problems;

(e) to pay special regard to the research needs of industries that lack an adequate scientific background, and to research problems that are common to more than one industry;

(f) to carry out particular researches, in co-operation with industry wherever possible, which will enable the stations to appreciate industry's problems more fully, and to recognise those fields in which more basic research is most urgently needed;

(g) to provide for industry, national and international standards of measurement of various fundamental physical quantities (such as length, mass and time), related secondary standards and reference materials;

(h) to conduct research on matters of broad public interest.

Each station selects certain of these functions to suit the particular conditions in which it operates so that the pattern of research varies greatly from one station to another. For the general nature of the research carried out in such establishments the reader is referred to the literature. [39, 40, and 41].

It will be seen that such establishments have a fair measure of freedom to follow at least some lines of enquiry for their technical interest or at least for reasons not immediately connected with profitability. Nevertheless there is, and should be, a constant traffic between them and other research activities in the country which can be an appreciable factor in improving scientific knowledge and advancing the frontiers of technology.

In some cases these laboratories will accept sponsored work from outside bodies such as industry or other government establishments. This they will conduct on the necessary basis of commercial security. This is in line with the present government policy of increasing work of a contractor–customer nature rather than performing instructed work only.

The principal laboratories in this group are:

Department of Trade and Industry
  Birniehill Institute, East Kilbride (Advanced Machine Tool and Central Technology)
  Safety in Mines Research Establishment, Buxton
  National Physical Laboratory, Teddington
  National Engineering Laboratory, East Kilbride
  Laboratory of the Government Chemist
  Computer Aided Design Centre

Warren Spring Laboratory, Stevenage

Home Office
  Central Forensic Science Laboratory, Aldermaston
  Regional Forensic Science Laboratories

Department of the Environment
  Road Research Laboratory, Middlesex
  Building Research Station, Watford
  Fire Research Station, Boreham Wood
  Princes Risborough Laboratory (Forest Products), Ayles-
    bury
  Hydraulics Research Station, Wallingford
  Water Pollution Research Laboratory, Stevenage

RESEARCH SPONSORED BY THE DEPARTMENT OF EDUCATION
AND SCIENCE

Much of government-financed research work is carried out by
the Research Councils who receive grants directly from the
Secretary of State for Education and Science to foster research
and training in the fields specified in their Charters. They are
the Agricultural Research Council (ARC), Medical Research
Council (MRC), Natural Environment Research Council
(NERC), Science Research Council (SRC) and Social Science
Research Council (SSRC).

The latter three were established in 1965. The Science Research Council supports research projects in pure and applied
science including nuclear energy and space research. The
Natural Resources Research Council is responsible for the
work of the Nature Conservancy, the Geological Survey and
the Soil Surveys and for research into long-term forestry,
oceanography, hydrology, fisheries and related aspects of
aquatic biology.

A Council for Science Policy was also set up in 1965 as a
body of scientific experts to advise the Secretary of State for
Education and Science about the formation and execution of
Government Science Policy. One of the main tasks of the CSP
has been to advise on the distribution of funds between the five
Research Councils. This was replaced by the Advisory Board
for the Research Councils, with similar functions, in late 1973.

TABLE 4.1   SCIENCE VOTE ESTIMATES 1971–2

	£(Millions)	% of total
ARC	18.704	16.0
MRC	23.015	19.6
NERC	15.888	13.6
SRC	55.733	47.5
Natural History Museum	1.877	1.6
Science: Grants and Services*	2.030	1.7
Total	117.247	100.0
SSRC	4.141	

* Includes grants to Royal Society, Royal Society of Edinburgh and the office for Scientific and Technical Information (DSTI).

The Research Councils operate in many ways including:

(a) Provision of grants to support work undertaken in university departments.

(b) To support students after their first degree working for research degrees,

(c) By the establishment of research units, usually in or near a university and sometimes staffed by university staff but sometimes established as separate establishments.

(d) By the provision of expensive experimental facilities used by university workers such as the Rutherford High Energy Physics Laboratory of the SRC.

Most of the Research Council research units are included in Table 4.1 but the principal laboratories are as follows:

Science Research Council
   Royal Radio and Space Research Station, Bucks
   Rutherford High Energy Laboratory, Didcot
   Daresbury Nuclear Physics Laboratory
   Atlas Computer Laboratory, Didcot

Medical Research Council
   National Institute for Medical Research, Mill Hill, London

Agricultural Research Council
   Rothamsted Experimental Station, Herts
   Agricultural and Horticultural Research Station, Bristol

East Malling Research Station
Welsh Plant Breeding Station, Aberystwyth
National Institute of Agricultural Engineering, Beds and
   Midlothian
Animal Breeding Research Institute

Natural Environment Research Council
   Institute of Geological Sciences
   Institute of Hydrology
   National Institute of Oceanography

LABORATORIES OF THE PUBLIC CORPORATIONS

There are, in Britain, a number of organisations functionally involved in science and technology which are in a sense 'official' without being government departments. These are concerned with general services to the country. The principal ones are:

   The Coal Board – which covers its subsidiary the British Coal Utilisation Research Association
   The Gas Council – which has the Midlands Research Station, Solihull, the London Research Station at Fulham and the Engineering Research Station, Newcastle upon Tyne
   The Electricity Council, with their Research Centre at Capenhurst
   The Central Electricity Generating Board with the Central Electricity Research Laboratories at Leatherhead, the Berkeley Nuclear Laboratories, Glos and the Central Engineering Laboratories, Marchwood
   The British Steel Corporation with its Inter-group Research Laboratories (BISRA) at various regional sites
   The United Kingdom Atomic Enginery Authority, which is a separate body, generally supervised by the Secretary of State for Trade and Industry, maintains a powerful array of laboratory facilities, notably the Atomic Energy Research Establishment, Harwell; the Atomic Energy Establishment, Winfrith; the Dounreay Experimental Reactor Division; the Fusion Research Laboratory, Culham; the Reactor Engineering Laboratory at Risley and the Reactor Development Laboratory at Windscale.

RESEARCH ASSOCIATIONS

Another group of laboratories of particular interest to industrial research, though also of interest to researchers generally, are those of the research associations (RAs). The term refers to two types of organisation. Firstly, there are those which used to be grant-aided, deriving their income partly from Government Departments (most usually the Department of Trade and Industry). The Government grant scheme has now been dropped and they are self-financing, receiving grants in the form of membership subscriptions and payments for specific items of work. In general the membership groupings which constitute such a research association are product or industry centred (as the British Ceramic Research Association) or technology centred (as the Production Engineering Research Association). Membership is usually open to Commonwealth, or even foreign countries. They are listed together with various data about them, in Appendix 4.2 (see end of chapter).

Secondly, there are a number of co-operative industrial research associations financed only by their industrial members usually very small and numbering less than twenty. These are listed in Appendix 4.3 but will not be further considered.

The research associations, which used to be grant-aided, were started in 1917 with the recognition by industry and government that industrial technology was deficient in many areas, particularly for war purposes. Government grants were provided in relation to industrial support with the original intention that they should become self supporting in five years' time. This, however, has never materialised, although the proportion of grant income has reduced. They were to be legally the responsibility of their members, each being controlled by a council elected by the members. In the main this still represents the structure of RAs today. They have had a chequered history. By 1925 they totalled 20 but between 1922 and 1928 more associations were wound up than formed. The year 1940 saw a new upsurge in numbers and income, rising to 50 in the early sixties with their total income first reaching £10m in 1963. That would appear to have been their high point in one sense, for closures and mergers have now reduced their numbers to just over 30. Their income has, however, continued to increase with an expenditure of £16.517 in 1969/70 or just under 1½ per cent of total national expenditure on R & D and a rate of growth in excess of that of national R & D expenditure. Individual RAs vary widely, the largest having an income of about £2m and the smallest about £50,000.

The types of work in which RAs engage include:

(a) General programme – co-operative work undertaken in the interests of all the membership, results of which are freely available and published to members.

(b) Member services – normally an information service which performs the dual role of supplying unsolicited information to members and answering technical queries posed by them.

It would be confidential to the sponsoring member, but it is not included for grant assessment.

(d) Group project work, of various types but the essence of which is that it is sponsored by a group of members with a common interest in a particular problem, who therefore share the expense. It is usually subject to a limited period of confidentiality before results become freely available – and it attracts Government grant.

The evolution of the RAs appears to be in the direction of an increasing concentration of effort on the latter two types of operation. The general programme is likely to diminish but there are strong reasons why it should not disappear altogether, including the strong desirability that the smaller firms should continue to obtain a service (with subscription levels adjusted to the new conditions) and to serve as a source of technical stimulation and creativity for the association as a whole in the hope that this will both attract good research workers and provide a source from which ideas for sound group projects might emerge.

The basis of support by Government having been changed, the Research Requirements Boards of the Department of Industry, as part of their overall remit can now offer work to RA's as contractors, on the customer-contractor principle, also the RAs are free to suggest projects to the Boards. It can be expected that there will be continuing support for some general programmes and for missionary activities to new member firms as well as support for substantial group projects.

Also during 1972–3 the Department of Trade and Industry relinquished its control over the admission of foreign firms to membership of RAs who are now free to admit them to full membership at a subscription level fixed by each RA. This should assist the RAs to develop an appropriate policy for overseas activities, especially with regard to the European Economic Community.

During 1972–3 an enquiry into research associations was led by the Earl of Bessborough [42] and among the conclusions and recommendations are:

1. That the money devoted to RAs has produced handsome benefits for industry and the economy and that this type of co-operative research should continue.

2. That the customer–contractor principle should be acceptable if interpreted in a liberal sense.

3. That there is a need for a greater central linking between all RAs which are at present linked only by a fairly informal Conference of Industrial Research Associations – and that a Board of Industrial Research and Development should be created. Also that a closer linkage with Trade Associations should be encouraged.

4. That the relationship between the RAs and the various government research establishments should be made more effective and that work of industrial importance should be more closely associated with RAs. (In the author's view a close relationship is entirely desirable but the RAs are no match for the large multi-disciplinary laboratories such as in the UKAEA for achieving major advances in industrial technology.)

5. That further mergers of RAs should be considered in order to achieve economies of scale in cases of membership overlap or technical compatibility.

6. That the RAs should more closely associate themselves with the marketing problems of their industries.

The managers of any R & D activities, particularly industrial research laboratories, should take careful note of the RAs which appertain to their operations to examine how member-ship could prove an effective supplement to their own activi-ties, particularly in group research activities. If membership of one or more RAs is decided upon, then maximum benefit should be derrived from it by careful assessment of the services available and by seeking positively to influence the pro-grammes of interest. [43] The RAs are most significant in in-dustries where the technology advances more slowly, such as ships, clothing, construction, textiles and non-ferrous metals, where they spend over 10 per cent of all R & D money.

Research associations have come in for much criticism in the past and their history is admittedly not one of perpetual success. It will be very interesting to see if the new formulae for their direction now emerging provide a more stable and satis-factory set-up.

A well-supported, well-directed research association can certainly be expected to contribute to its industry a large fund of scientific knowledge relevant to its materials and processes, to discover profitable solutions to some at least of its major communal problems, and to introduce into common practice a growing number of scientific and technological innovations as well as providing a 'sponsored' research avenue with special skills related to its industry. For its team of technologists to remain stimulated and forward looking it is necessary that a regular stream of challenging scientific and technological work in the forefront of their field should continually be coming to them.

SPONSORED RESEARCH INSTITUTES

While the sponsoring of research work on to other estab-lishments provides an interplay which nowadays is fostered by nearly all laboratories to some extent, there are a number of in-stitutes privately operated and free from government control, the so-called sponsored research institutes which exist solely for the purpose of carrying out specific research projects on behalf of clients. The work has no other purpose than to further the interests of clients, it is carried out with as much confidentiality as the sponsor requires and often a large measure of the profits of such operations are ploughed back into improving the facilities offered to clients.

This sort of institution is used more widely in the USA than in the UK but it is now growing considerably over here, both in terms of the numbers of institutes and facilities available and in the extent of their use. The advantages are that the sponsoring organisation can effectively employ specialist staff in a given field for a short time, thus avoiding taking on more staff on a temporary basis or otherwise disrupting the normal work of their research department.

Similarly they will be effectively hiring rather than buying the laboratory facilities and equipment that are required.

The principal sponsored research institutes operating in the UK at present are:

International Research and Development Co. ˙Ltd, Newcastle
Huntingdon Research Centre
Sondes Place Research Institute, Dorking
Robertson Research International Ltd
Ricardo and Co. (Engineers) Ltd, Slough
Fulmer Research Institute Ltd, Stoke Poges
Arthur D. Little Research Institute, Midlothian
J. A. Radley Research Institute, Reading
Yarsley Laboratories Ltd
Inneresk Research International
Cambridge Consultants Ltd

CONSULTANTS

The service given by sponsored institutes is of course closely akin to the service given by consultants either as firms with laboratory facilities or as individuals. There are few industries which do not have such consultancies available. Whether these can be considered as scientific services or not obviously depends on the individuals performing the service but in general they are disseminators of scientific know-how rather than an actual scientific service – but nonetheless valuable for that (see Chapter 10). Many consultants are members of the Association of Consultant Scientists, London.

THE NATIONAL RESEARCH DEVELOPMENT CORPORATION (NRDC)

The NRDC is a public body supervised by the Department of Trade and Industry. It was established in 1949 by the Development of Inventions Act 1948 (now consolidated in the DOI Act 1967) with the function of developing and exploiting inventions resulting from research paid for out of public funds and also inventions from other sources which were not being sufficiently developed or exploited. Later the Corporation was empowered to promote or assist research likely to lead to an invention, and under further legislation passed in 1965 it was given powers to carry out projects at the request of a government department for which it would either be paid a fee or guaranteed against loss. NRDC is required to have regard for the public interest, generally to be defined as to the general economic benefit of the country, and is required to break even financially except in so far as this definition of the public interest requires otherwise. Advances of capital up to £50m may be made by the Department of Trade and Industry for NRDC's activities.

One of the prime reasons for setting up NRDC was for the exploitation of inventions arising from the government's own research establishments. The Research Councils also agreed to assign most of their inventions to NRDC as do the universities. It thus becomes a means of exploiting so-called 'spin-off' ideas.

Another of the purposes of setting up NRDC was to assist the private inventor if his invention seemed to justify support. This might be done simply by putting the inventor in touch with industrial companies who might be interested – a method also adopted sometimes with inventions arising from government laboratories, etc. It might also be done by setting up subsidiary companies for the exploitation, particularly where the invention is likely to have a high financial gain factor but is highly speculative. Fuel cells, hovercraft and tracked hovercraft are examples of such enterprises.

Another function of NRDC was the setting up, with industry, of joint ventures based on the invention of an individual firm. In such a joint venture NRDC normally contributes half the cost of a specified development and expects to recover its outlay, with profit, if the venture succeeds. The total expenditure of NRDC on all these activities approximated to £7.4m in 1970/71.

RESEARCH IN INDUSTRY

As we have seen, the largest amount of research in the UK is conducted in private manufacturing industry, although this is heavily contributed to financially by the government. Also industry conducts most of its research internally with relatively small amounts being farmed out to research associations, universities, etc.

As would be expected, research activities in private firms are of many different types. Some large groups, with a number of operating divisions, might have a corresponding number of research laboratories appropriate to their particular operations. Others might have central research facilities only, while others still might have some peripheral facilities as well as a central research institute.

Industries differ too in the extent to which they concentrate on the development of ideas bought from other sources, or themselves conduct relatively basic research to give rise to their own innovation. In general the science-based industries are more likely to operate some fairly basic research. An outstanding example is the development of nylon, which started out as basic research, mission-orientated towards new fibres by Carruthers, but which was not successfully developed to marketing point until after ten years and the expenditure of £3,000,000 by the Du Pont Corporation.

In general, however, industry is likely to be concerned with improving the products and processes it sells and evolving new ones to meet market conditions, either within a standard framework or towards a diversification of a firm's activities.

This by no means exhausts the list of organisations or institutions available to give firms scientific advice or service.

There are many trade associations (e.g. the Zinc Development Association) which exist for the promotion of the use of their firm's products, doing so by information and technical service activities both to members and prospective customers.

Similar service to customers is given by major firms and indeed in the case of very many small firms it is a very valuable way in which they can receive the benefits of science. There are a number of ways in which this occurs, ranging from the regular visit of the technical salesman of a supplying firm to point out the advantages which accrue from the use of a newly-developed product (rather as the great drug houses acquaint doctors of new medicaments) to the sort of arrangement where the designer of a new process or machine will install it in the factory of a potential customer for a controlled experiment to be carried out.

Finally, of course, we should not forget the tremendous scientific literature of the learned societies, as they are called, the technological press, and the bulletins and pamphlets of supplying firms. The volume of literature has grown so tremendously in recent years that it is a problem which has exercised many international conferences as to how to codify, index, abstract and distribute to be of maximum use. What is certainly true, however, of such literature is that it is not very likely to be of direct advantage to a firm unless there are scientists in the firm who can interpret the data and develop it into a suitable form for application to the firm's activities.

SOCIAL IMPLICATIONS OF SCIENCE

It is becoming increasingly recognised that the application of new knowledge must be done in harmony with the economic and human needs of the situation it affects, and this is just as true of new industrial processes as of more far-reaching advances like nuclear energy. To this end a closer collaboration can be envisaged in the future between research establishments' activities and those of the Social Science Research Council, jointly working with the other Research Councils, so that the implications of advances can receive adequate consideration from the overall social point of view (see Chapter 10).

It is clear that there is a very great diversity of forms in which research and development is carried out in the UK. The director of any one unit needs to have some awareness of the options open to him in seeking advice, placing external research contracts, or merely enlarging the knowledge of himself and his staff. Then he has to formulate his own pattern of communication, to extract the most out of all the facilities available to him in relation to the purpose of his laboratory.

SUMMARY

In this chapter a short account is given of the general ways in which research is carried out in the UK, paying particular attention to the best ways of using them in the interests of any particular research organisation.

The majority of fundamental work is carried out in the universities which have the most rapidly expanding research budget. There are many advantages in any effort being associated with some university work and the many ways in which appropriate contact can be formulated are given.

Government research comes next as a body of basic or new mission-orientated research work and again it is desirable to consider which way any research department can derive advantage by associating with such government research. The much discussed subject of 'spin-off' from advanced R & D such as is practised in government laboratories is considered in its many aspects.

The industrial research associations are undergoing a rapidly changing pattern in recent years with more mergers and techniques of association, a greater freedom to associate with overseas companies, the application of the customer–contractor relationship and greater encouragement of group research and sponsored research activities as present tendencies.

Sponsored research institutes and consultants are briefly dealt with and the function and operation of the National Research Development Council is described.

It is necessary for any research management to formulate its own pattern of communication with those various centres of research activity.

APPENDIX 4.1   RESEARCH INSTITUTES, ESTABLISHMENTS AND
UNITS SHOWN MAPPED IN FIG. 4.1*

Aberdeen

Macaulay Institute for Soil Research	ARC
Rowett Research Institute	ARC
Unit of Statistics	ARC
Obstetric Medicine Research Unit	MRC
Institute of Marine Biochemistry	NERC
Mountain and Moorland Ecology Station, Institute of Terrestrial Ecology	NERC
Marine Laboratory	DAFS
Torry Research Station	Min. of Agriculture, Fisheries and Food

Aylesbury and Bedford region

National Institute of Agricultural Engineering, Silsoe	ARC
Propellants Explosives and Rocket Motor Establishment, Westcott	Min. of Defence
Royal Aircraft Establishment, Bedford	Min. of Defence
Forest Products Research Laboratory, Princess Risborough	Dept. of the Environment

Bangor, N. Wales, Gwynedd

Unit of Embryology	ARC
Bangor Research Station, Institute of Terrestial Ecology	NERC
Unit for Marine Invertebrate Biology	NERC

Birmingham

Industrial Injuries and Burns Research Unit	MRC
Neuropharmacology Research Unit	MRC
Unit for Research on the Chemical Pathology of Mental Disorders	MRC
Unit for Research on the Experimental Pathology of the Skin	MRC

Brighton

Unit of Nitrogen Fixation	ARC
Royal Greenwich Laboratory, Herstmonceux	SRC

Bristol

Agricultural and Horticultural Research Station, Long Ashton	ARC
Dental Research Unit	MRC

Cambridge

Institute of Animal Physiology, Babraham	ARC
Plant Breeding Institute	ARC

* Updated Jan. 1979, eliminating stations no longer in existence and using latest titles.

Statistics Group – Department of Applied Biology	ARC
Unit of Reproductive Physiology and Biochemistry, Animal Research Station	ARC
Unit of Soil Physics	ARC
Abnormal Haemoglobin Research Unit	MRC
Applied Psychology Research Unit	MRC
Chemotherapy Research Unit	MRC
Department of Experimental Medicine	MRC
Dunn Nutritional Laboratory	MRC
Laboratory of Molecular Biology	MRC
Strangeways Research Laboratory	MRC
National Institute of Agricultural Botany	Min. of Agriculture, Fisheries and Food
Computer Aided Design Centre	DOI

Cardiff

Epidemiological Research Unit	MRC
Pneumoconiosis Research Unit, Penarth	MRC

Christchurch

Royal Signals and Radar Establishment	Min. of Defence
Military Engineering Experimental Establishment	Min. of Defence

Edinburgh

Animal Breeding Research Organisation	ARC
Animal Diseases Research Association	ARC
Hill Farming Research Organisation	ARC
Scottish Institute of Agricultural Engineering	ARC
Poultry Research Centre	ARC
Scottish Plant Breeding Station	ARC
Unit of Animal Genetics	ARC
Brain Metabolism Research Unit	MRC
Clinical Effects of Radiation Research Unit	MRC
Clinical Endocrinology Research Unit	MRC
Mutagenesis Research Unit	MRC
Unit for Research in the Epidemiology of Psychiatric Illness	MRC MRC
Institute of Geological Sciences, Regional Office	NERC
Institute for Marine Environmental Research Oceanographic Laboratory	NERC
Royal Observatory	SRC
Royal Botanic Gardens	Min. of Agriculture, Fisheries and Food

Farnborough

National Gas Turbine Establishment	Min. of Defence
Royal Aircraft Establishment	Min. of Defence
Institute of Aviation Medicine	Min. of Defence

Glasgow

Atheroma Research Unit	MRC
Cell Genetics Research Unit	MRC
Experimental Virus Research Unit	MRC
Scottish Marine Biological Association – Marine Research Laboratory, Oban, Argyll	NERC
National Engineering Laboratory, East Kilbride	Dept. of Industry
Road Research Laboratory, East Kilbride	Dept. of the Environment

Harwell region

Radiobiological Laboratory, Letcombe Regis, Wantage	ARC
Radiobiological Research Unit	MRC
Atlas Computer Laboratory, Chilton	SRC
Rutherford Laboratory, Chilton	SRC
Atomic Energy Establishment, Culham	UKAEA
Atomic Energy Research Establishment	UKAEA
Isotope Research Laboratory, Wantage	UKAEA

Hertfordshire region

John Innes Institute, Norwich	ARC
Rothamsted Experimental Station, Harpenden	ARC
Plant Pathology Laboratory, Harpenden	Min. of Agriculture, Fisheries and Food
Services Electronics Research Laboratory, Baldock	Min. of Defence
Building Research Station, Watford	DOE
Warren Spring Laboratory, Stevenage	Dept. of Industry

Kent region

East Malling Research Station, nr Maidstone	ARC
Systematic Fungicides Unit, Ashford	ARC
Wye College Dept. of Hop Research, Ashford	ARC
Royal Armament R & D Establishment, Sevenoaks	Min. of Defence

Leeds

Environmental Radiation Research Unit	MRC
Mineral Metabolism Research Unit	MRC
Institute of Geological Sciences, Regional Office	NERC

London

26 MRC Units	MRC
National Institute for Medical Research, Mill Hill	MRC
Institute of Geological Sciences	NERC
National Institute of Geology	NERC
National Maritime Institute, Feltham	DOI
Laboratory of the Government Chemist	DOI
Food Science Branches	Min. of Agriculture, Fisheries and Food

Royal Botanic Gardens, Kew	Min. of Agriculture, Fisheries and Food
Salmon and Freshwater Fisheries Laboratory	Min. of Agriculture, Fisheries and Food
Explosives and Rocket Motor Establishment, Waltham Abbey	Min. of Defence
Centre for Overseas Pest Research	Min. of Overseas Development Administration
Tropical Products Inst., Tropical Pest HQ and Information Unit	Min. of Overseas Development
Post Office Research Station, Dollis Hill	Post Office
National Physical Laboratory, Teddington	Dept. of Industry
British Museum (Natural History)	
Zoological Society of London	

Newcastle upon Tyne

Demyelinating Diseases Research Unit	MRC

Oxford

Weed Research Organisation, Yarnton	ARC
Blood Coagulation Research Unit	MRC
Body Temperature Research Unit	MRC
Bone-seeking Isotopes Research Unit	MRC
Cell Metabolism Research Unit	MRC
Cellular Immunology Research Unit	MRC
Neuroendocrinology Research Unit	MRC
Population Genetics Research Unit	MRC
Psycholinguistics Research Unit	MRC

Porton, Wilts

Chemical Defence Establishment	Min. of Defence
Microbiological Research Establishment	Min. of Defence
Tropical Pesticides Research Unit	Overseas Development Administration

Portsmouth

Admiralty Surface Weapons Establishment	Min. of Defence
RN Physiological Laboratory	Min. of Defence

Reading region

Grasslands Research Institute, nr Maidenhead	ARC
Institute for Research on Animal Diseases, Compton	ARC
National Institute for Research in Dairying, Shinfield	ARC
Rheumatism Research Unit	MRC
Hydrological Research Unit	NERC

Atomic Weapons Research Establishment, Aldermaston	Min. of Defence
NAAS Laboratories, Coley Park	Min. of Agriculture, Fisheries and Food
Meteorological Office, Bracknell	Min. of Defence
Home Office Research Unit	Home Office
Hydraulics Research Station, Wallingford	DOE

Slough region

Pest Infestation Control Laboratory, Slough	ARC
Appleton Laboratory, Slough	SRC
Road Research Laboratory, West Drayton	Dept. of the Environment
Tropical Stored Products Centre	Overseas Development Administration

Surrey region

Animal Virus Research Institute, Pirbright	ARC
Laboratory Animals Research Unit, Carshalton	MRC
Neurophyschiatric Research Unit	MRC
Toxicology Unit, Carshalton	MRC
Virus Research Unit, Carshalton	MRC
Institute of Oceanographic Science, Wormley Laboratory	NERC
Pest Infestation Control Laboratory, Surbiton	Min. of Agriculture, Fisheries and Food
Central Veterinary Laboratory, New Haw, Weybridge	Min. of Agriculture, Fisheries and Food
Defence Operational Analysis Organisation, West Byfleet	Min. of Defence
Military Vehicles and Engineering Establishment, Chertsey	Min. of Defence
Forestry Com. Research Station, Alice Holt Lodge, Farnham	Forestry Com.
Directorate of Overseas Surveys	Min. of Overseas Development Administration

Warrington

Daresbury Laboratory	SRC
Atomic Energy Authority, Risley	UKAEA

Individual Establishments

Monks Wood Experimental Station, Institute of Terrestial Ecology, Abbots Ripton, Hunts	NERC
Welsh Plant Breeding Station, Aberystwyth	ARC

Hannah Research Institute, Ayr	ARC
Ministry of Agriculture, Government of Northern Ireland, Belfast	
Two further divisions in Hillsborough, Co. Down and Loughgall, Co. Amagh, also the Agricultural Research Institute of N. Ireland, Hillsborough. There is also a Regional Office of the Institute of Geological Sciences in Belfast	NERC
Clinical Psychiatry Research Unit, Chichester, Sussex	MRC
Shellfish Laboratory, Conway	Min. of Agriculture, Fisheries and Food
Scottish Horticultural Research Institute, nr Dundee	ARC
Naval Construction Research Establishment, Dunfermline	Min. of Defence
Carcinogenic Substances Research Unit, Exeter	MRC
Merlewood Research Station, Institute of Terrestrial Ecology, Grange-over-Sands, Cumbria	NERC
Admiralty Materials Laboratory, Holton Heath, Dorset	Min. of Defence
Houghton Poultry Research Station, nr Huntingdon	ARC
Microbial Systematics Research Unit, Leicester	MRC
Glasshouse Crops Research Institute, Littlehampton Sussex	ARC
Unit for Research on Occupational Aspects of Ageing, Liverpool	MRC
Fisheries Laboratory, Lowestoft	Min. of Agriculture, Fisheries and Food
Royal Signals and Radar Establishment, Malvern, Worcs.	Min. of Defence
Food Research Institute, Norwich	ARC
Freshwater Fisheries Laboratory, Pitlochry, Perth	Scottish Office
Marine Biological Association of the UK, Plymouth Institute for Marine Environmental Research	NERC
Reactor Fuel Element Laboratories, nr Preston	UKAEA
Safety in Mines Research Establishment, Sheffield	Dept. of Employment
Royal Military College of Science, Shrivenham, Wilts	Min. of Defence
National Vegetable Research Station, Wellesbourne, Warwicks	ARC
Freshwater Biological Ass. Laboratory, Windermere Laboratory	NERC
Atomic Energy Establishment, Winfrith Heath, Dorset	UKAEA

APPENDIX 4.2 LIST OF RESEARCH ASSOCIATIONS (JAN 1979)

Field of main activity *Official title* *Abbreviations used by RA*		*Address*	*Directors*
CAST IRON British Cast Iron Research Association	Headquarters and laboratories	Bordesley Hall Alvechurch nr Birmingham B48 7QB	Director: H. Morrogh, Esq., C.B.E., F.I.M., F.I.B.F., D.Sc.(h.c.) F.R.S.
	Scottish laboratory	Blantyre Industrial Estate Glasgow G72 0UP	Superintendent: A. N. Sumner, Esq., A.I.M.
CERAMICS British Ceramic Research Association	Office	Queens Road Penkjull Stoke on Trent ST4 7LQ	Director of Research: A. Dinsdale, Esq., O.B.E., M.Sc., F.Inst.P. F.I.Ceram.
COKE British Carbonization Research Association	Laboratories Test plant and office	Wingerworth Chesterfield Derbyshre S42 6JS	Director: J. P. Graham, Esq., B.Sc., F.Inst.F.
	Other associated laboratories	Northern Coke Research Committee The University of Newcastle upon Tyne	
COMPUTERS National Computing Centre Ltd (NCC)		Oxford Road Manchester M1 7ED	Director: D. Firnberg, Esq.

Name		Address	Directors
COTTON, SILK & MAN-MADE FIBRES			
The Cotton Silk & Man-Made Fibres Research Association	Laboratories	Shirley Institute Didsbury Manchester M20 8RX	Director: L. A. Wiseman, Esq., O.B.E., B.Sc., A.R.I.C., F.T.I.
CUTLERY			
Cutlery & Allied Trades Research Association (CATRA)	Laboratory	Henry Street Sheffield S3 7EQ	Director of Research: E. A. Oldfield, Esq., A.Met., M.I.M., M.Inst.Pkg.
	Office	Light Trades House Melbourne Avenue Sheffield S10 2QJ	
DROP FORGING			
Drop Forging Research Association (DFRA)		Shepherd Street Sheffield S3 7BA	Director: S. E. Rogers, Esq., Ph.D., B.Sc., F.R.I.C.
ELECTRICAL			
Electrical Research Association (ERA)	Laboratories and office	The Electrical Research Assoc. Cleeve Road Leatherhead Surrey KT22 7SA	Director: B. C. Lindley, Esq., B.Sc. (Eng.), Ph.D., F.I.Mech.E., F.I.E.E, F.Inst.P.
FABRIC			
Fabric Care Research Association Ltd		Forest House Laboratories Knaresborough Road Harrogate North Yorkshire NGZ 7LZ	Director of Research: E. J. Davies, Esq., B.Sc., M.Sc.

FLOUR MILLING & BAKING The Flour Milling & Baking Research Association	Laboratories and office	Research Station Chorleywood Rickmansworth Herts WD3 5SH	Director: B. Spenser, Esq., B.Sc., M.A., Ph.D., Sc.D., M.R.I.A.
FOOD British Food Manufacturing Industries Research Association (BFMIRA)	Laboratories and office	Randalls Road Leatherhead Surrey KT22 7RY	Director: A. W. Holmes, Esq., B.Sc., Ph.D., F.R.I.C., F.I.F.S.T.
FRUIT & VEGETABLE Campden Food Preservation Research Association (previously Fruit & Vegetable Preservation R.A.)	Laboratories and office	Chipping Campden Gloucestershire GL55 6LD	Director: H. R. Hinton, Esq., M.Sc., B.Sc., F.I.Biol.
FURNITURE Furniture Industry Research Association (FIRA)	Office, technical information service and research	Maxwell Road Stevenage Herts SG1 2EW	Director: D. M. Heughan, Esq., M.Sc. (Cantab.), B.Sc. (Dunelm), C.Eng., M.I.Mech.E., A.F.R.AeS., M.B.I.M., M.I.M.C.
GLASS British Glass Industry Research Association (BGIRA)	Laboratories office	Northumberland Road Sheffield S10 2UA	Director: C. Thorpe, Esq., B.Sc. (Tech.), F.S.G.T.
HOSIERY Research Centre for Knitting, Dyeing and Make up (previously Hosiery & Allied Trades Research Association)	Laboratories and office	Thorneywood 7 Gregory Boulevard Nottingham NG7 6LD	Director: G. K. Mecklenburgh, Esq., B.Sc., C.Chem., M.R.I.C.

Name		Address	Directors
HYDROMECHANICS British Hydromechanics Research Association (BHRA)	Laboratory and office	Cranfield Bedford Beds MK43 0AJ	Director: G. F. W. Adler, Esq., B.Sc.(Eng.), D.I.C., C.Eng., F.I.Mech.E.
LEATHER British Leather Manufacturers' Research Association (BLMRA)	Laboratories and office	Milton Park Stroude Road Egham Surrey TW20 9UQ	Director: R. L. Sykes, Esq., Ph.D., F.R.I.C.
LINEN Lambeg Industrial Research Association (LIRA)	Laboratories and office	The Research Institute Lambeg, Lisburn Co. Antrim N. Ireland	Director: H. A. C. Todd, Esq., O.B.E., B.Sc., F.R.Stat.Soc., F.T.I.
MACHINE TOOLS Machine Tool Industry Research Association (MTIRA)	Laboratories and office	Hulley Road Hurdsfield Macclesfield Cheshire SK10 2NE	Director: A. E. de Barr, Esq., O.B.E., B.Sc., F.Inst.P., C.Eng., F.I.Mech.E.
MOTOR VEHICLES Motor Industry Research Association (MIRA)	Laboratories, office and proving ground	Watling Street Nuneaton Warwickshire CV10 0TU	Director: C. Ashley, Esq., Ph.D., C.Eng.
NON-FERROUS METALS BNF Metals Technology Centre (BNF)	Laboratories and office	The Grove Laboratories Denchworth Road Wantage, Oxon OX12 9BJ	Director: Dr R. Johnston

PAINT		
Paint Research Association (previously Research Assoc. of British Paint, Colour & Varnish Manufacturers)	Laboratories and office	The Paint Research Station Waldegrave Road Teddington Middlesex TW11 8LD	Director: G. de W. Anderson, Esq., B.Sc., Ph.D., F.R.I.C., A.R.P.S.

PAPER & BOARD, PRINTING & PACKING		
The Research Association for the Paper & Board, Printing & Packaging Industries (PIRA)	Laboratories and office	PIRA House Randalls Road Leatherhead Surrey KT22 7RU	Director: N. K. Bridge, Esq., B.Sc., Ph.D., F.Inst.P.

PRODUCTION ENGINEERING		
Production Engineering Research Association of Great Britain (PERA)	Laboratories and office	Melton Mowbray Leics LE13 0PB	Director: D. F. Galloway, Esq., C.B.E., Ph.D., Wh.Sch.Pres. I.Mech.E., M.I.E.E., M.I.Prod.E, Mem.A.S.M.E., B.Sc.(Hons.), M.Inst.Pet.

RUBBER & PLASTICS		
Rubber & Plastics Research Association of Great Britain (RAPRA)	Laboratories and office	Shawbury Shrewsbury Shropshire SY4 4NR	Director: J. P. Berry, Esq., B.Sc., Ph.D., F.P.R.I.

SCIENTIFIC INSTRUMENTS		
Sira Institute Ltd. (SIRA)	Laboratories and office	South Hill Chislehurst Kent BR7 5EH	Director: S. S. Carlisle, Esq., M.Sc., C.Eng, F.I.E.E., F.Inst.P.

Name	Address	Directors
SHIPS British Ship Research Association	Laboratory and office	Wallsend Research Station Wallsend Tyne and Wear NE28 6UY	Director: J. C. Asher, Esq.

Name		Address	Directors
SHIPS British Ship Research Association	Laboratory and office	Wallsend Research Station Wallsend Tyne and Wear NE28 6UY	Director: J. C. Asher, Esq.
SHOES Shoe & Allied Trades Research Association (SATRA)	Laboratories and office	Satra House Rockingham Road Kettering Northants NN16 9JH	Director: J. G. Butlin, Esq., B.Sc., F.Inst.P., A.R.T.C.S., F.B.S.I.
SPRINGS Spring Research and Manufacturers Association (SRMA)	Headquarters and Laboratories	Henry Street Sheffield S3 7EQ	Director of Research: J. A. Bennet, Esq., B.Sc., M.Inst.P.
STEEL CASTINGS Steel Castings Research and Trade Association (SCRATA)	Research station and office	East Bank Road Sheffield S2 3PT	Director: J. A. Reynolds, Esq., B.Sc., Ph.D., F.I.B.F., F.I.M.
TOXICOLOGY British Industrial Biological Research Association		Woodmansterne Road Carshalton Surrey SM5 4DS	Director: R. F. Crampton, Esq., Ph.D., M.B., M.R.C.P., F.I.Biol.
WELDING The Welding Institute (WI)	Research station	Abington Hall Abington nr Cambridge CB1 6AL	Director-General: A. A. Wells, Esq., F.R.S., Ph.D., C.Eng., M.I.Mech.E., F.Weld.I.

WOOL
Wira (previously
Wool Industries
Research Association)

Laboratories
and office

Headingley Lane
Leeds LS6 1BW

Director: B. E. King, Esq., B.Sc.,
Ph.D., M.I.E.E.

Member services
unit (Scotland)

Netherdale Industrial
Estate
Galashiels
Selkirkshire TD1 3EY

MYCOLOGY
Commonwealth
Mycological Institute

Laboratories
and office

The Commonwealth
Mycological Institute
Ferry Lane
Kew
Surrey TW9 3AF

Director: A. Johnston, Esq., B.Sc.,
A.I.C.T.A.

APPENDIX 4.3 COOPERATIVE INDUSTRIAL RESEARCH ASSOCIATIONS

Name	Address	Directors
Brick Development Association	Woodside House Winkfield Windsor Berkshire SL4 2DR	Director-General: 　J. Scott McBride, Esq.
British Brush Manufacturers' Research Association	c/o Department of Textile Industries The University Leeds LS2 9JT	Director: D. I. Fothergill, Esq.
The British Internal Combustion Engine Research Institute Ltd.	111–112 Buckingham Avenue Slough SL1 4PH	Director: A. G. Jaquiss, Esq.
Building Services Research and Information Association	Old Bracknell Lane Bracknell Berks RG12 4AH	Director: P. A. Coles, Esq.
Cement and Concrete Association	Wexham Springs Slough SL3 6PL	Director-General: 　The Hon Leo Russell C.B.E., 　T.D.
Construction Industry Research and Information Association	6 Storey's Gate London SW1P 3AU	Director: L. S. Blake, Esq, Ph.D., B.Sc. (Eng), F.I.C.E., F.I.Struct.E., F.I.H.E.

Processors' and Growers' Research Organisation	The Research Station Great North Road Thornaugh Peterborough PE8 6HJ	Director: A. J. Gane, Esq.
Shipowners' Refrigerated Cargo Research Association	140 Newmarket Road Cambridge CB5 8HE	Director: K. C. Hales, Esq.
Timber Research and Development Association	Hughenden Valley High Wycombe Buckinghamshire HP14 4ND	Director: J. G. Sunley, Esq., M.Sc., F.I.Struct.E., F.I.W.Sc.
Water Research Centre	Ferry Lane Medmenham Marlow Bucks SL7 2HD	Director: R. G. Allen, Esq., O.B.E., B.Sc., Ph.D., F.Iust.P.
Water Research Centre	45 Station Road Henley-on-Thames Oxfordshire RG9 1BW	Director: J. L. van der Post, Esq.
Water Research Centre	Stevenage Laboratory Elderway Stevenage Hertfordshire SG1 1TH	Assistant Director: C. E. Eden, Esq.

NATURAL ENVIRONMENT RESEARCH COUNCIL

Institute of Geological Sciences:

Southern Regional Office
Kensington London

S.W. District Office
Exeter

Geochemical Division
London WC1

Geophysical Division
London SW7

Global Seismology Unit
Edinburgh

Geomagnetism Unit
Royal Greenwich Observatory
Sussex

Experimental Cartography Unit:

London SW7

Institute of Oceanographic Sciences:

Bidston Laboratory
Birkenhead

Taunton Laboratory
Taunton Somerset

Instrumentation and Equipment Services Division
NERC Research Vessel Base
Barry Glamorgan

Whale Research Unit
British Museum London

Institute for Marine Environmental Research:
Seals Research Division
c/o Fisheries Laboratory
Lowestoft

Institute of Hydrology:
Crowmarsh Gifford
Wallingford
Oxfordshire

Freshwater Biological Association:
River Laboratory
Wareham
Dorset

Culture Centre of Algae and Protozoa:
Cambridge

Institute of Terrestrial Ecology:
Furzebrook Research Station
Wareham Dorset

Coastal Ecology Research Station
Norwich

Brathens Research Station
Aberdeen

Institute of Tree Biology:
Edinburgh

Unit of Invertebrate Virology:
Oxford

British Antarctic Survey:
London SW1

AGRICULTURAL RESEARCH COUNCIL INSTITUTES

Name	Address	Directors
Animal Breeding Research Organisation	West Mains Road Edinburgh EH9 3JQ	Director: J. W. B. King, Esq, Ph.D., F.R.S.E.
Institute of Animal Physiology	Babraham Cambridge CB2 4AT	Director: B. A. Cross, Esq., M.A., Ph.D., Sc.D, M.R.C.V.S., F.R.S.
Institute for Research on Animal Diseases	Compton Newbury Berkshire RG16 0NN	Director: J. M. Payne, Esq., B.Sc., Ph.D., M.R.C.V.S.
Food Research Institute	Colney Lane Norwich NR4 7UA	Director: R. F. Curtis, Esq., B.Sc., Ph.D., D.Sc., F.R.I.C.
Letcombe Laboratory	Letcombe Regis Wantage Oxfordshire OX12 9JT	Director: R. Scott Russell, Esq., C.B.E., Ph.D., D.Sc, F.I.Biol.
Meat Research Institute	Langford Bristol BS18 7DY *and* Weston Laboratory Bridge Road Weston-super-Mare Somerset	Director: Professor J. R. Norris, B.Sc., Ph.D., F.I.Biol.

Poultry Research Centre

King's Buildings
West Mains Road
Edinburgh
EH9 3JS

Director: T. C. Carter, Esq, O.B.E.,
M.A., Ph.D., D.Sc., F.I.Biol.,
F.R.S.E.

Weed Research Organization

Begbroke Hill
Sandy Lane
Yarnton
Oxford
OX5 1PF

Director: J. D. Fryer, Esq., M.A.

AGRICULTURAL RESEARCH COUNCIL UNITS

Name	Address	Directors
Unit of Animal Genetics	Institute of Animal Genetics West Mains Road Edinburgh EH9 3JN	Director: Professor D. S. Falconer, Sc.D., F.I.Biol., F.R.S.E., F.R.S.
Unit of Invertebrate Chemistry and Physiology	University of Sussex Falmer Brighton Sussex BN1 9QT	Honorary Director: Professor A. W. Johnson, Sc.D., F.R.S.
(Subgroup) Unit of Invertebrate Chemistry and Physiology	University of Cambridge Department of Zoology Downing Street Cambridge CB2 3EJ	Associate Director: J. E. Treherne, Esq., M.A., Ph.D., Sc.D.
Unit of Muscle Mechanisms and Insect Physiology	Department of Zoology University of Oxford South Parks Road Oxford OX1 3PS	Honorary Director: Professor J. W. Pringle, M.B.E., Sc.D., F.R.S.
Unit of Nitrogen Fixation	University of Sussex Brighton Sussex BN1 9QT	Director: Professor J. Chatt, M.A., Ph.D., Sc.D, F.R.S.
Unit of Statistics	University of Edinburgh James Clerk Maxwell Building The King's Buildings	Honorary Director: Professor D. J. Finney, M.A., Sc.D, F.R.S.E, F.R.S.

Statistics Group

Mayfield Road
Edinburgh
EH9 3JZ

Systemic Fungicides Unit

Department of Applied Biology
Downing Street
Cambridge
CB2 3DX

Wye College
Ashford
Kent
TN25 5AH

Officer in Charge: J. G. Rowell, Esq.,
M.A.

Honorary Director:
Professor R. L. Wain, C.B.E.,
Ph.D., D.Sc., F.R.I.C.,
F.R.S.

STATE-AIDED INSTITUTES
ENGLAND AND WALES

Name	Address	Directors
Animal Virus Research Institute	Pirbright Woking Surrey GU24 0NF	Director: J. B. Brooksby, Esq., C.B.E., D.Sc., M.R.C.V.S., F.R.S.E.
East Malling Research Station	East Malling Maidstone Kent ME19 6BJ	Director: Professor A. F. Posnette, C.B.E., M.A., Ph.D., Sc.D., F.I.Biol., F.R.S.
Glasshouse Crops Research Institute	Worthing Road Rustington Littlehampton Sussex BN16 3PU	Director: D. Rudd-Jones, Esq, M.A., Ph.D., F.I.Biol.
Grassland Research Institute	Hurley Maidenhead Berkshire SL6 5LR	Director: Professor A. Lazenby, M.Sc., M.A., Ph.D., F.T.S., F.I.Biol.
Houghton Poultry Research Station	Houghton Huntingdon PE17 2DA	Director: P. M. Biggs, Esq, Ph.D., D.Sc., M.R.C.V.S., M.R.C.Path., F.I.Biol., F.R.S.
John Innes Institute	Colney Lane Norwich NR4 7UH	Director: Professor R. Markham, M.A., Ph.D., F.R.S.

Long Ashton Research Station

Long Ashton
Bristol
BS18 9AF

Director: Professor J. M. Hirst, D.Sc.,
Ph.D., F.R.S.

National Institute of Agricultural
Engineering

Wrest Park
Silsoe
Bedford
MK45 4HS

Director: R. L. Bell, Esq., B.Sc.,
Ph.D., F.I.M., F.Inst.P.

National Institute for Research in
Dairying

Shinfield
Reading
RG2 9AT

Director: Professor J. W. G. Porter,
B.A., Ph.D.

National Vegetable Research Station

Wellesbourne
Warwick
CV35 9EF

Director: Professor J. K. A. Bleasdale,
B.Sc., Ph.D.

Plant Breeding Institute

Maris Lane
Trumpington
Cambridge
CB2 2LQ

Director: Professor R. Riley, D.Sc.,
F.I.Biol., F.R.S.

Rothamsted Experimental Station

Harpenden
Herts
AL5 2JQ

Director: L. Fowden, Esq., Ph.D.,
F.I.Biol., F.R.I.C., F.R.S.,

Welsh Plant Breeding Station

Plas Gogerddan
Aberystwyth
Cardiganshire
SY23 3EB

Director: Professor J. P. Cooper,
M.Sc., Ph.D., D.Sc.,
F.I.Biol., F.R.S.

Wye College, Department of Hop
Research

Ashford
Kent
TN25 5AH

Head of Department:
R. A. Neve, Esq., B.Sc.,
Ph.D., Dip.Agr.Sci.

SCOTLAND

Name	Address	Directors
Animal Diseases Research Association	Moredun Institute 408 Gilmerton Road Edinburgh EH17 7JH	Director: J. T. Stamp, Esq., C.B.E., D.Sc., F.R.C.V.S., F.R.S.E.
Hannah Research Institute	Ayr KA6 5HL	Director: Professor J. A. F. Rook, Ph.D., D.Sc., F.R.I.C., F.I.Biol., F.R.S.E.
Hill Farming Research Organisation	Bush Estate Penicuik Midlothian EH26 0PH	Director: J. M. M. Cunningham, Esq., B.Sc. (Agric)., Ph.D., F.R.S.E.
Macaulay Institute for Soil Research	Craigiebuckler Aberdeen AB9 2QJ	Director: Professor T. S. West, B.Sc., Ph.D., D.Sc., C.Chem., F.R.I.C.
Rowett Research Institute	Bucksburn Aberdeen AB2 9SB	Director: Sir Kenneth L. Blaxter, D.Sc., F.R.S.E, F.R.S.
Scottish Horticultural Research Institute	Invergowrie Dundee DD2 5DA	Director: C. E. Taylor, B.Sc., Ph.D., F.I.Biol., F.R.S.E.
Scottish Institute of Agricultural Engineering	Bush Estate Penicuik Midlothian EH26 0PH	Director: D. P. Blight, Esq., M.Sc., Ph.D., M.I.Mech.E.
Scottish Plant Breeding Station	Pentlandfield Roslin Midlothian	Director: Professor R. C. F. Macer, M.A., Ph.D.

MEDICAL RESEARCH COUNCIL ESTABLISHMENTS

Name	Address	Directors
National Institute for Medical Research	Mill Hill London NW7 1AA	Director: Sir Arnold Burgen, M.D., F.R.C.P., F.R.S.
Clinical Research Centre	Watford Road Harrow Middlesex HA1 3UJ	Director: C. C. Booth, Esq., M.D., F.R.C.P.
MRC Applied Psychology Unit	15 Chaucer Road Cambridge CB2 2EF	Director: A. D. Baddeley, Esq., Ph.D.
MRC Biochemical Parasitology Unit	Molteno Institute Downing Street Cambridge CB2 3EE	Director: B. A. Newton, Esq., M.A., Sc.D., M.R.C.Path., F.I.Biol., F.R.I.C.
†MRC Blood Group Reference Laboratory *(Administered by the Council for the Department of Health and Social Security)*	Gatliff Road off Ebury Bridge Road London SW1W 8QJ	Director: †K. L. G. Goldsmith, Esq., M.B, Ph.D, M.R.C.P., M.R.C. Path. Carolyn Giles, Ph.D. (Acting Director)
MRC Blood Group Unit	University College London Wolfson House 4 Stephenson Way London NW1 2HE	Director: Ruth Sanger, Ph.D., F.R.S.

†The Management of the Laboratory passed formally to the Health Department on 1 Oct. 1977.

Name	Address	Directors
MRC Blood Pressure Unit	Western Infirmary Glasgow G11 6NT	Director: A. F. Lever, Esq, M.B., B.Sc., F.R.C.P., F.R.S.E.
MRC Brain Metabolism Unit	University Department of Pharmacology 1 George Square Edinburgh EH8 9JZ	Director: G. W. Arbuthnott, Esq., Ph.D.
MRC Cell Biophysics Unit	Department of Biophysics University of London King's College 26–29 Drury Lane London WC2B 5RL	Honorary Director: Professor M. H. F. Wilkins, C.B.E., Ph.D., F.R.S.
MRC Cell Mutation Unit	University of Sussex Falmer Brighton BN1 9QG	Director: Professor A.B. Bridges, Ph.D., F.I.Biol.
MRC Cellular Immunology Unit	Sir William Dunn School of Pathology Oxford OX1 3RE	Director: A. F. Williams, Esq., Ph.D.
MRC Clinical Genetics Unit	Institute of Child Health 30 Guilford Street London WC1N 1EH	Director: Professor C. O. Carter, D.M., F.R.C.P.
MRC Clinical Oncology and Radiotherapeutics Unit	Medical School Hills Road	Honorary Director: Professor N. M. Bleehen,

	Cambridge CB2 2QH	B.Sc., B.M., F.R.C.P., F.R.C.R.
MRC Clinical Pharmacology Unit	University Department of Clinical Pharmacology Radcliffe Infirmary Woodstock Road Oxford OX2 6HE	Honorary Director: Professor D. G. Grahame- Smith, M.B, Ph.D, F.R.C.P.
MRC Clinical and Population Cytogenetics Unit	Western General Hospital Crewe Road Edinburgh EH4 2XU	Director: Professor H. J. Evans, Ph.D., F.R.S.E.
MRC Clinical Psychiatry Unit	Graylingwell Hospital Chichester Sussex PO19 4PQ	Director: P. Sainsbury, Esq., M.D., F.R.C. Psych, F.R.C.P., D.P.M.
MRC Cyclotron Unit	Hammersmith Hospital DuCane Road London W12 0HS *and* Western General Hospital Crewe Road Edinburgh EH4 2XU	Director: D. D. Vonberg, Esq., B.Sc.
MRC Demyelinating Diseases Unit	Newcastle General Hospital Westgate Road Newcastle upon Tyne NE4 6BE	Acting Director: E. A. Caspary, Esq., M.Y.S.C., M.R.C. Path.

Name	Address	Directors
MRC Dental Unit	Dental School Lower Maudlin Street Bristol BS1 2LY	Honorary Director: Professor A. I. Darling, C.B.E., D.D.Sc., M.D.S., F.D.S.R.C.S., M.R.C.S., F.R.C. Path.
†MRC Dental Epidemiology Unit	The London Hospital Medical College Turner Street London E1 2AD	Honorary Director: Professor G. L. Slack, C.B.E., D.D.S., F.D.S.R.C.S., D.I.P. Bact.
MRC Unit on the Development and Integration of Behaviour	Subdepartment of Animal Behaviour Madingley Cambridge CB3 8AA	Honorary Director: Professor R. A. Hinde, M.A., Sc.D., D.Phil., F.R.S.
MRC Developmental Neurobiology Unit	Institute of Neurology 33 John's Mews London WC1N 2NS	Director: R. Balázs, Dr. Med., Dr. Phil.
MRC Developmental Psychology Unit	Drayton House Gordon Street London WC1H 0AN	Director: N. O'Connor, Esq., Ph.D.
Dunn Nutrition Unit	Milton Road Cambridge CB4 1XJ *and*	Director: R. G. Whitehead, M.A., Ph.D, F.I.Biol.

†Disbanded 30 September 1977

MRC Unit for the Study of
Environmental Factors in Mental and
Physical Illness

Dunn Clinical Nutrition Centre
Adderbrooke's Hospital
Trumpington Street,
Cambridge
CB2 1QE

Director: J. W. B. Douglas, Esq.,
B.M., B.Sc.

MRC Environmental Physiology Unit

London School of Economics
and Political Science
20 Hanway Place
London
W1P 0AJ

Director: Professor J. S. Weiner,
D.Sc., F.R.C.P., F.I.Biol.

MRC Epidemiology Unit (South
Wales)

London School of Hygiene and
Tropical Medicine
Keppel Street
London
WC1E 7HT

Director: P. C. Elwood, Esq., M.D.,
M.R.C.P., F.F.C.M.

MRC–DHSS Epidemiology and
Medical Care Unit

4 Richmond Road
Cardiff
CF2 3AS

Director: T. W. Meade, Esq., M.A.,
B.M., M.R.C.P., F.F.C.M.

MRC Unit for Epidemiological
Studies in Psychiatry

Northwick Park Hospital
Watford Road
Harrow
HA1 3UJ

Director: N. B. Kreitman, Esq., M.D.,
M.R.C.P.E., F.R.C. Psych.,
D.P.M.

MRC Experimental Haematology Unit

University Department of Psychiatry
Royal Edinburgh Hospital
Morningside Park
Edinburgh
EH10 5HF

Director: Professor P. L. Mollison,
M.D., F.R.C.P., F.R.C. Path.,
F.R.S.

St Mary's Hospital Medical School
London
W2 1PG

Name	Address	Directors
MRC Unit on the Experimental Pathology of Skin	The Medical School University Birmingham B15 2TJ	Director: C. N. D. Cruickshank, Esq., M.D., M.R.C.P., F.R.C. Path, D.I.H.
†MRC Gastroenterology Unit	Central Middlesex Hospital Park Royal London NW10 7NS	Director: E. N. Rowlands, Esq., M.D., B.Sc., F.R.C.P.
MRC Hearing and Balance Unit	Institute of Neurology National Hospital Queen Square London WC1N 3BG	Director: J. D. Hood, Esq., Ph.D., D.Sc., F.Inst.P.
MRC Human Biochemical Genetics Unit	The Galton Laboratory (University College London) Wolfson House 4 Stephenson Way London NW1 2HE	Acting Director: D. A. Hopkinson, Esq., MD.
MRC Immunochemistry Unit	University Department of Biochemistry South Parks Road Oxford OX1 3QU	Honorary Director: Professor R. R. Porter, Ph.D., F.R.S.
MRC Industrial Injuries and Burns Unit	Birmingham Accident Hospital Bath Row Birmingham B15 1NA	Director: J. P. Bull, Esq., C.B.E., M.D., F.R.C.P.

†Disbanded 30 September 1977

MRC Institute of Hearing Research

University Medical School
Nottingham
NG7 2UH

Director: Professor M. P. Haggard,
Ph.D.

MRC Laboratories, The Gambia

PO Box 273, Fajara
The Gambia
West Africa

Director: I. A. McGregor, Esq., C.B.E.,
F.R.C.P., F.F.C.M.,
D.T.M. & H.

MRC Laboratories, Jamaica

University of the West Indies
Mona Kingston 7
Jamaica

Director: G. R. Serjeant, Esq., M.D.,
M.A., M.R.C.P.

MRC Laboratory Animals Centre

Medical Research Council
Laboratories
Woodmansterne Road
Carshalton
Surrey
SM5 4EF

Director: J. Bleby, Esq., B.Vet.Med.,
M.R.C.V.S., F.I.Biol.

MRC Leukaemia Unit

Royal Postgraduate Medical School
DuCane Road
London
W12 0HS

Honorary Director:
D. A. G. Galton, Esq., M.D.
F.R.C.P.

MRC Lipid Metabolism Unit

Hammersmith Hospital
DuCane Road
London
W12 0HS

Director: N. B. Myant, Esq., D.M.,
B.Sc., F.R.C.P.

MRC Mammalian Development Unit

Wolfson House
University College
London
4 Stephenson Way
London
NW1 2HE

Director: Anne McLaren, D.Phil.,
F.R.S.

Name	Address	Directors
MRC Mammalian Genome Unit	University Department of Zoology West Mains Road Edinburgh EH9 3JT	Director: Professor P. M. B. Walker, C.B.E., B.A., Ph.D.
MRC Medical Sociology Unit	Institute of Medical Sociology Westburn Road Aberdeen AB9 2ZE	Director: Professor R. Illsley, Ph.D.
MRC Unit for Metabolic Studies in Psychiatry	University Department of Psychiatry Middlewood Hospital PO Box 134 Sheffield S6 1TP	Director: Professor F. A. Jenner, M.B., Ph.D., D.P.M., M.R.C.P., F.R.C. Psych.
MRC Mineral Metabolism Unit	The General Infirmary Great George Street Leeds LS1 3EX	Director: Professor B. E. C. Nordin, M.D., D.Sc., F.R.C.P.
MRC Laboratory of Molecular Biology	The Medical School Hills Road Cambridge CB2 2QH	Director: M. F. Perutz, Esq., C.H., C.B.E., Ph.D., F.R.S., (Chairman of Governing Board)
MRC Unit on Neural Mechanisms of Behaviour	3 Malet Place London WC1E 7JG	Director: I. S. Russell, Esq., Ph.D.
MRC Neurochemical Pharmacology Unit	University Department of Pharmacology	Director: L. L. Iversen, Esq., M.A., Ph.D.

	Hills Road Cambridge CB2 2QD	
MRC Neurological Prostheses Unit	Institute of Psychiatry De Crespigny Park Denmark Hill London SE5 8AF	Director: Professor G. S. Brindley, M.D, F.R.C.P., F.R.S.
MRC Neuropharmacology Unit	The Medical School Birmingham B15 2TJ	Director: Professor P. B. Bradley, D.Sc.
MRC Perceptual and Cognitive Performance Unit	Experimental Psychology Laboratory University of Sussex Falmer Brighton BN1 9QY	Director: Professor W. P. Colquhoun, Ph.D.
MRC Pneumoconiosis Unit	Llandough Hospital Penarth Glamorgan CF6 1XW	Director: P. C. Elmes, M.D., F.R.C.P.
MRC Radiobiology Unit	Harwell, nr Didcot Oxfordshire OX11 0RD	Director: J. Vennart, Esq., D.Sc., F.Inst.P.
MRC Reproduction and Growth Unit	Princess Mary Maternity Hospital Newcastle upon Tyne NE2 3BD	Director: Professor A. M. Thomson, M.B., B.Sc., F.R.C.O.G., D.P.H.
MRC Reproductive Biology Unit	2 Forrest Road Edinburgh EH1 2QW	Director: Professor R. V. Short, Sc.D., F.R.C.V.S., F.R.S., F.R.S.E.

Name	Address	Directors
MRC Social and Applied Psychology Unit	Department of Psychology University of Sheffield Sheffield S10 2TN	Director: P. B. Warr, Esq., Ph.D.
MRC Social Psychiatry Unit	Institute of Psychiatry De Crespigny Park Denmark Hill London SE5 8AF	Director: Professor J. K. Wing, M.D., Ph.D., D.P.M., F.R.C. Psych.
MRC Statistical Research and Services Unit	University College Hospital Medical School 115 Gower Street London WC1E 6AS	Director: I. Sutherland, Esq., M.A., D.Phil.
MRC Toxicology Unit	Medical Research Council Laboratories Woodmansterne Road Carshalton Surrey SM5 4EF	Director: T. A. Connors, Esq., Ph.D., D.S.C., F.I.Biol.
MRC Trauma Unit	Stopford Building University of Manchester Oxford Road Manchester M13 9PL and Hope Hospital Eccles Old Road Salford Manchester M6 8HD	Director: Professor H. B. Stoner, M.D., B.Sc., F.R.C.Path.

MRC Unit for Laboratory Studies of Tuberculosis

Royal Postgraduate Medical School
DuCane Road
London
W12 0HS

Director: Professor D. A. Mitchison, M.B., F.R.C.P., F.R.C. Path.

MRC Tuberculosis and Chest Diseases Unit

Brompton Hospital
Fulham Road
London
SW3 6HP

Director: Wallace Fox, Esq., C.M.G., M.D., F.R.C.P., F.F.C.M.

MRC Virology Unit

Institute of Virology
Church Street
Glasgow
G11 5JR

Director: Professor J. H. Subak-Sharpe, Ph.D., F.R.S.E.

MRC Vision Unit

School of Biological Sciences
University of Sussex
Falmer
Brighton
BN1 9QY

Director: Professor H. J. A. Dartnall, D.Sc., F.R.I.C.

Medical Research Council Laboratories

Woodmansterne Road
Carshalton
Surrey
SM5 4EF

Director: F. W. Matthews (Administrative officer)

5 The choice of an R & D portfolio

Research and development are seldom nowadays pursued for their own sake. Even the universities, still the centres of the most basic research, would accept that they have a role of underpinning British science through the production of trained research workers and the setting up of a framework of scientific knowledge. In most other cases, however, the role of R & D is even more directly related to the strategy of the parent organisation.

There are three basic situations where an R & D role is called for to assist in overall strategy:

(a) Where the objective has been decided in some definite form and R & D is to be one of the tools for achieving it. The objective might be the building of a supersonic air liner or cheapening a chemical plant process by a certain method.

(b) Where the objective is known in some general way but has not been defined in a form from which the R & D programme will be dictated. Thus the objective might be, as in the research associations, to improve the profitability of a group of industries or it might be, as in the Department of Health and Social Security, to improve the control of illness relative to its cost to the community.

(c) Where the objective is not known. It might be that a technological advance is sought, in defence, agriculture, industry, etc., and one is looking for a scientific concept upon which an R & D programme might be based to apply it. Examples of this in the past are nuclear energy, electromagnetic transmission, etc., but it is in the nature of science, of course, that we cannot know what ideas will prove to be worth developing in the future.

OBJECTIVE DECIDED

In situation (a) the most important matter is to choose the right project – the right aircraft, weapon, nuclear reactor, etc. This can only be done with a combination of a background of wide-ranging strategic research available and the right quantitative tools for forecasting costs and rewards. The larger the project, the more widespread and deep does the exploratory research need to be so that development costs can be reasonably estimated, and the more sophisticated does the market analysis need to be, and it is in itself a very difficult problem to decide at what point the move from strategic research to a project shall be made. Too lengthy preliminary studies will cost too much and maybe cause the project to miss the market. Too little, and the project development costs estimates will be wrong so that the profitability may vanish. Some of the aircraft developments of recent years, in particular, seem to indicate faulty judgement in this area. When the project has been decided upon, the research and development necessary to create the technology will largely decide itself. It will be a matter of determining where the gaps are, endeavouring to fill them from existing or purchasable knowledge, perhaps reconceiving the design so that the knowledge is not required and finally arriving at the necessary research programme which looks amenable to successful conclusion on the required timescale. This is a continuing process since gaps in knowledge might be filled by new work available from outside, research success might prove obdurate so that further design change might be necessary, or the knowledge one hoped to buy might prove inadequate and a further research programme prove necessary.

The more ambitious a project the greater the uncertainty in costs of R & D and the time to complete, as indicated in the following table.[14]

TABLE 5.1   RATIO OF FINAL COST TO INITIAL ESTIMATES

Fighters	1.7
Bombers	3.0
Cargoes and tankers	1.2
Missiles	5.2

With very large projects this inability accurately to estimate the cost and time to completion has been of considerable concern and has led to the development of formal, mathematical systems of project selection, the elements of which will be described in this chapter.

However, in this situation the R & D content of the overall project follows from the detailed statement of how the project is to be carried out. (It is assumed that sufficient basic and exploratory research has been done to justify, with a reasonable chance of success, going ahead with the objective.) This detailed statement will give a list of R & D tasks of various degrees of complexity, varying between mission-orientated research and development that will be necessary before the objective can be fully accomplished.

The next problem will be to decide where the different R & D tasks are to be carried out. This will depend on the men, resources and skills available 'in-house' which cannot be even more usefully employed on some other task, and whether some of the tasks might not be better carried out elsewhere, as when specialised skills are needed for a short time or when special resources are available elsewhere, or where the economics are such that it is cheaper to do it somewhere else. In the event of deciding that some of the R & D should be 'contracted out', the next step would be to choose a likely 'contractor' from those described in Chapter 4 and make the necessary contractual arrangements. It may be that suitable arrangements cannot be made by contracting out and the in-house situation would have to be reviewed, perhaps taking on more staff and building more facilities for the work to be carried out.

In this way, with any particular objective a research portfolio will be drawn up with a section for in-house work and a section for work contracted out and it will be necessary to establish project leadership to keep the overall objective clearly in mind and to dovetail the in-house and contracted out work.

The case where the objective is defined is undoubtedly the easiest in principle for which to draw up the research portfolio.

OBJECTIVE KNOWN GENERALLY

In the second situation we first have to interpret the overall objective to restate it as a defined objective (or as a series of objectives). This is by far the most usual situation that a research establishment finds itself in and the task of restatement into defined objectives which best suit the overall strategy of the parent authority is the most difficult to be undertaken and success or failure in this largely decides the overall success or failure of the research establishment.

The first step, although it may appear obvious, is to know what the overall objective is. It may be nothing more complicated than to make as much money for the parent authority as possible, but it may be much more complicated. The Department of Health and Social Services will be concerned to save money on its National Health bill or at least to increase the value of the service it gives without the spend going up. It may, therefore, legitimately determine where the highest economic cost occurs and see whether there is enough scientific knowledge available upon which to base a research project to reduce that cost – by eliminating the disease which causes it, for instance. But it might be argued that improvements where suffering is gauged to be greatest is a more legitimate basis for selecting a research portfolio in the health field. What is almost certainly true, though not always appreciated, is that scientific interest in a research problem is not likely to be the best criteria from a social point of view for such a selection to be made – nor is the emotive demand of public opinion for a particular cure that happens to have caught the public consciousness. There are obviously many other complicatory factors in determining the research objectives of the Department of Health and Social Security.

Another example relates to forensic science for the Home Office. It has to be considered whether the main legitimate objective is the prevention of crime or its detection and ideas for a research portfolio explored accordingly.

A very good example of assessing the operations of an industry to find where the greatest costs are and which might be reduced by R & D and then formulating a research programme has been described by J. Leicester, Director of the

British Laundries Research Association, who by those methods changed the pattern of research conducted by the BLRA to be much more useful to the industry. [44]

Another example is the author's analysis of the costs involved in uranium extraction from its ores together with cost /benefit analysis to lay down a research portfolio for reduction in uranium ore extraction costs. [45]

Having formulated the objectives satisfactorily the next step is to parade the project ideas that are available and assess them against the objectives. The project ideas that are paraded need to be of two types. The first, as indicated above, is where the activities of the 'present organisation' are analysed to see if this gives rise to areas where an R & D attack would yield large dividends.

The second type is where an idea is created from within a research context and its exposure and consideration indicates that it is a candidate for advancing the objectives of the parent organisation. This is the more difficult because even the best research workers tend to work on the basis of elaboration of known ideas. In so doing they may well uncover a new concept but the process of recognising it as forming the basis of a solution to some practical problem not necessarily within their ken, and therefore as an innovation in technology, has never been easy. Much has been written on the sources of technological innovation, and it seems clear that the needs of the 'market' are more likely to stimulate such innovation than the scientific value of an idea itself.[46]

There can be no rules about how such ideas are formulated. What is important is that the ideas should be of a type which can be advanced by R & D and that people who are good at thinking out such ideas are put into a position where they know enough of the affairs of the parent organisation and of research generally to be able to associate the two. In general a research director is likely to be chosen because he has some flair for picking out the right projects, but he in his turn needs to manipulate his resources so that such project ideas can be engendered.

OBJECTIVE UNKNOWN

The third situation is an extension of the above on a wider canvas. The scientific ideas that formed the basis of nuclear energy were not explored by the electricity supply authorities with the objective of improving the sources of power. Their development was well advanced for military purposes before they become candidates for power supply improvement. The really novel advances tend to come from outside the work directed to the known objectives of an organisation. Within an organisation they can only be fostered by maintaining a sophisticated communication network between scientists of different disciplines and in different fields and also between working scientists and superintending scientists well tuned to the objectives of the overall organisation.

With these as the principal situations in which research and development project ideas are formulated in a strategic context, it has to be remembered that they do not appear so clear-cut in practice.

What is a definite objective to one layer of an organisation may not be recognised as such by another layer. Thus a Ministry of Defence objective might be a new method of moving troops, but unless it turned out to be an aircraft or a vehicle or a tank – recognised objectives of the appropriate laboratories – it might be regarded as a research idea without a development objective in any one of these laboratories. Also, the process of carefully analysing an operation to decide the best point of R & D attack may expose a good project idea, but an alternative more original scientific concept might serve the project better.

Whatever the strategic situation, therefore, it is important both to communicate the real objectives as widely as practicable and to mount a commensurate network by which original scientific ideas are more likely to find their market. It is also important to give breathing space to the more ambitious projects and the more novel ideas, for although these are likely to be more costly and of a lower degree of certainty and are not usually the favoured topics, for instance, of industry (see page 24), they are the projects which are likely to give the more handsome rewards on the longer-term basis and therefore to maintain the viability of an organisation, whether it be an industrial company or a country's defence, into the future.

SOURCE OF NEW RESEARCH IDEAS

An analysis of American industry was made by R. E. Seiler [15] to explore the source of new research ideas. The results are summarised in Table 5.2.

Additionally it is Seiler's view that the research staff contributes a noticeably greater proportion of research ideas in the chemical and pharmaceutical industries than in the metallurgical and manufacturing industries and the government contributes a much heavier proportion of ideas in the electronic and aerospace industries.

In general, however, this indicates that in industry generally, while the major source of new ideas is reckoned to be the research department itself, nevertheless by far the majority opinion is that fruitful research ideas do come from many other sources. Thus it will be noted that 17.6 per cent of firms think that 6–10 per cent of their ideas come from customers. There is no reason to suppose that this is not true of other types of research than industrial. Indeed, in those spheres in which the objective is only known generally it is even more likely that outside ideas might be useful.

ESTABLISHING CANDIDATE PROJECTS FOR ULTIMATE SELECTION OF A PORTFOLIO

We have thus seen how broad strategical considerations can lead in principle to the uncovering of areas in which research is likely to pay off in terms of the 'parent authority's' objectives. The mechanisms by which such ideas can be generated and then followed by the formulation of definite research topics in keeping with these ideas have next to be considered.

There is no real substitute for the situation where communication between scientists and managers and between managers and higher staff are so thorough that all new ideas can be guaranteed to filter backwards and forwards. But this is an ideal which can only be aimed at and alternative methods must also be sought.

It will be desirable to set up discussion groups within one's own organisation, and preferably together with representatives of the parent organisation and possibly outside con-

TABLE 5.2 PERCENTAGE OF COMPANIES INDICATING IDEAS RECEIVED

	No ideas	5%	6-10%	11-20%	21-40%	41-60%	61-80%	81-100%
Research staff	0.1	0.0	1.9	6.7	19.2	27.9	27.9	16.4
Sales staff	16.1	12.5	23.2	25.9	16.1	4.5	1.7	0.0
Customers	51.0	18.6	17.6	7.8	3.9	1.1	0.0	0.0
Government	71.6	9.8	4.9	9.8	2.9	1.0	0.0	0.0
Other management	29.7	20.8	19.8	15.8	11.9	2.0	0.0	0.0
Others	72.8	1.9	5.8	14.6	1.0	3.9	0.0	0.0

sultants, both to suggest the type of analysis that might be fruitful and to suggest the type of R & D projects which will best serve the objectives so uncovered. One will also seek to widen the potential solutions to problems by appropriate discussions outside one's organisation, perhaps in universities, government research establishments and the like.

BRAINSTORMING SESSIONS

One technique has become known as the brainstorming session which involves a meeting between scientists, their management and representatives of higher policy makers, together with consultants and other associates of the organisation such as the sales and engineering departments of a firm or their counterparts in other organisations. An atmosphere conducive to free expression of ideas is encouraged and the field of interest then discussed generally in the hope of cross-fertilisation of ideas and the marrying of vague scientific hunches with 'marketable' requirements. Brainstorming sessions need to have their own preparation and education and not to be considered by the researcher in the light of another time-wasting committee effort. The essence of the good brainstorming session is that it should be led in the direction of thinking widely and without constraint.

It is doubtful whether the group approach to the generation of creative ideas has more chance of fruitful results than the individual approach, but it is a technique which is not very time consuming and, particularly where the group includes outside men of excellence, can be approved of by researchers and yield at least some stimulation and cross-fertilisation of ideas.

Formal visits to laboratories where interested and knowledgeable associates of the organisation are invited to view what is going on in the laboratory and discuss the work of the scientists are another useful way of generating or exposing ideas both useful to the research and potentially exploitable. Since the largest proportion of research ideas is likely to come from the research department itself, it is particularly necessary to develop an environment in which creativity is likely to be stimulated. Steps that might be taken include:

(a) Allowing a proportion of the scientists' efforts for non-accountable work.

(b) Setting up mixed-discipline teams or at least making positive arrangements where people of different disciplines associate together.

(c) Recruiting personnel from other technologies.

(d) Continual awareness of the desirability of research staff knowing the objectives of the parent authority or, in other words, what the 'market' is looking for.

An aggressive use of patents is another method not greatly used in the UK, but to a much greater extent in the US and Japan for isolating possible new ideas for research projects. The technique is to associate patent agents, preferably especially skilled in such methods, when new ideas are being considered and then to mount an international patent search in that area of technology. Ideas may arise for which the exploratory research has already been carried out, which can then form the basis of a development project.

By the use of all these techniques the research management will be able to establish a parade of research project ideas which then need to be crystallised into definite research proposals.

SELECTION OF PORTFOLIO

The next step is to decide on the portfolio of projects which the department will undertake or sponsor. For it is most unlikely that it will be possible to undertake all the candidates. Indeed, if it is, then it is almost certain that insufficient effort has gone into the process of uncovering candidate projects.

It would be very comforting if the portfolio could then be chosen on mathematical lines and indeed much effort has been spent over the last ten years on formal methods of project description, resource allocation and benefit/cost ratios. Some of these techniques will be described later in this chapter, but it will be as well first to appreciate that one cannot simply and sufficiently line up the projects in order of cost effectiveness and form a portfolio from the top ones on the list, until the budget has been used up.

Some of the considerations that also come into play are:

(a) the best use of the skills available in the laboratories

(i) in the sense that some R & D can only be expected to be successful if particularly able people are employed while others might get by with lesser research ability.

(ii) in the sense that the particular expertise of the research workers has to be made use of. This is not to say that research workers are unable to change their field of work and in some cases it is desirable, both from a point of view of widening a man's experience and of introducing a cross-fertilisation effect, that this should be done. But to an appreciable extent research projects must be chosen in line with the expertise of the workers,

(iii) in the sense that sometimes in a laboratory there is a man or a small team with a very special expertise – perhaps something like electron optics – which also has special and expensive facilities which it may be highly desirable to maintain for the service they give to other projects. Such a team needs to be found work fully to occupy it, even though it may not be of highest benefit/cost ratio.

(b) the best use of the laboratory available. Frequently the cost of new facilities would be a major part of a research project budget which would rule out such projects in favour of those where expensive existing resources can be used.

(c) It is desirable that research projects should interact with each other and with the integrated experience of the laboratory as a whole. Projects should, therefore, be chosen so that the portfolio 'hangs together' in this sense and further enhances the corporate knowledge and prestige of the research department.

(d) It is frequently true of project-orientated research that the research is but one input to the successful accomplishment of a project and the project leader may well not be part of the research organisation at all. The direction and management of the research has, however, to be knowledgeable about the project as a whole in order to steer the research to the demands of the project. A research department which is involved in too many such projects totally different in character is very difficult effectively to direct so the research is not carried out as efficiently as should be. It is, therefore, desirable to choose research projects so that only a few form parts of wider projects led from outside while the majority have their principal activities and end-points largely within the department.

(e) The projects chosen must be suitable to the expertise of the research managers as well as the research workers and the expertise involved refer to the skills of judgement, management techniques, ability to control large numbers of projects, etc., as well as technical knowledge. Some research managers are brilliant at leading small teams and playing a large part in the scientific work themselves but with little judgement of the effect of their work on large projects. Others can handle large numbers of projects, managing them efficiently, making use of the latest management techniques but without themselves having a deep understanding of the work of the research workers under them.

(f) Some projects will be on a short time scale and others more lengthy and it is desirable that there should be a mixture in any portfolio so that the department as a whole is continually alive to the necessity of meeting end-dates; resources can be allocated on a relative priority basis, rather than intensive use being required for all at the same time, and the department can experience a successive series of successful events.

(g) The two broad divisions of R & D are (i) improvement of existing process or projects and (ii) new ideas for new processes or products. It is desirable to have a sound balance between these, for the first consolidates the expertise of the department and the second opens up new vistas gradually leading to new expertise being developed.

(h) Except at the beginning of a new laboratory, the activity of choosing a portfolio of research projects is one of continuously changing it as some projects are completed or new staff or funds arrive, rather than creating one *ab initio*. The choice may well, therefore, vary depending on what resources happen to be available at the time rather than what is economically the most important.

(i) Virtually all applied R & D laboratories, except those exclusively concerned with testing or technical service, sooner or later engage, overtly or clandestinely, in research which is not directly concerned with the programmes commissioned by the customers: and it is a good thing that they do. It is, however, important that such activities should be recognised as being necessary and that they should be formally quantified. The amount of time allowed for this is much open to discussion. It will be dependent on the type of organisation involved and will be greater where the search for new fields is continually valid and least where 'customer' requirements are clearly laid down.

Seiler [15] has analysed the existing (1964) situation in US industry, as summarised in Table 5.3.

TABLE 5.3   UNASSIGNED TIME ALLOWED TECHNICAL RESEARCH PERSONNEL—1964

% Time allowed	% of companies
None	2.8
5%	20.2
5–10%	45.0
10–15%	21.1
15–20%	10.0
20%	0.9

It will be seen that on optimum value is about 10 per cent and it is the writer's view that it should not usually amount to much more than this figure if management and control are to be usefully effected.

These activities are called general research because they do not necessarily consist of applied R & D or of basic research. General research is done for the following reasons:

(a) To engage in basic research in a field relevant to the applied tasks of the laboratory, but which is not being done elsewhere (e.g. at a university),

(b) To test out new, way-out and unprogrammed ideas of the scientists themselves,

(c) To maintain expertise, e.g. to recruit and keep a spectroscopist who will not join the laboratory unless he can spend part of the time on his own research,

(d) To facilitate the transition from academic life to that in an applied R & D organisation.

Such activities should be allowed for in any research and development portfolio. [13]

These considerations might be described as research orientated. That is, they arise from consideration of how best to use the research resources. Considerations will also arise related to the needs of the parent authority. Some of the factors which must be considered are:

(a) The desired direction of growth or evolution (geographical areas, product lines, spheres of influence).
(b) The desired rate of growth – related to the individual firm, the entire industry or even the national economy.
(c) The pressure of social factors – any organisation will need to pay more attention to projects which solve material and energy shortages, reduce pollution and eliminate unpopular jobs in the 1970s than previously.
(d) The degree of diversification desired within the parent authority (although the sale of technology engendered in the laboratory rather than its direct use can modify this).
(e) Degree of government control to be tolerated.
(f) The public image of the organisation.
(g) The degree of dependence on outside factors such as there being a limited number of suppliers or acceptable raw material sources.
(h) Priority might well be given to projects which will result in the optimum loading of production capacity, particularly in capital-intensive industries. Such a consideration should not, however, be allowed to discourage the really high gain factor advance because it will need new plant.
(i) Satisfying any appropriate criteria related to overriding considerations, e.g. labour shortages or space shortage. [47 and 15]
(j) The balance between offensive and defensive research. In any organisation areas must be selected in which it wants to hold a commanding position and areas in which it needs to be informed so that its competitors or its inquisitors cannot create an over-damaging situation. A guess will also

have to be made regarding areas which it can afford to disregard altogether.

STUDY OF AN ACTUAL PORTFOLIO IN USA INDUSTRY

Mansfield [14] reports the study of the laboratory portfolio of an electric/electronic manufacturer's central research laboratory operating in the United States, totalling $20m annually. The overall split was observed as shown in Fig. 5.1 and the following factors were found to obtain in the choice of individual research projects:

1. About half of the observed allocation of funds can be explained by a purely economic model – the assumption of expected profit maximisation (though this does not mean that they were only chosen in order of profits expected).
2. Decisions by company scientists reflecting their own scientific and professional goals which are not always consistent with the strictly commercial objectives of the firm.
3. Intra-firm politics are important (such as pleasing senior executives by carrying out their 'pet' projects).
4. At each level of decision, adjustments may be made to a project, particularly financial, so that the original designed objective of the project may be unattainable.

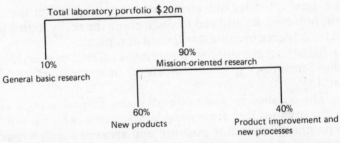

FIG. 5.1 Breakdown of research of central laboratory of a USA electronics firm

5. Because of the way projects tend to be judged, there is a tendency to concentrate on projects where it is likely that success can be claimed within a year.

6. Some scientists and departmental managers are more effective in mobilising support for their proposals.

There are thus many factors which enter into the actual choice of a portfolio when all the candidates have been lined up.

Some represent the exercise of wise and creative direction and others are perhaps not so commendable but clearly we do not have a correct picture if we believe that portfolios are, or should be, drawn up purely on a mathematical basis of calculating the economic advantages of each available project and opting for those which come 'top of the league'.

QUANTITATIVE ANALYTICAL METHODS OF PROJECT SELECTION

Nevertheless quantitative analytical methods are being increasingly used for selecting projects to a maximum economic advantage both for large projects (like the development of carbon fibres) where it is clearly foolish to allocate large funds and resources without having sound economic reasons for so doing, or for small projects where a real choice is available to a director from a number of alternative projects, so that a mathematical calculation of profit potential is a real guide to him. Basically the problem is to decide what return we can get from a given outlay on R & D. Logically, before we can calculate what will be the cost of a given project we have to be clear what the project is that we are costing. There are two steps towards this which require clear thinking if we are to achieve the optimum solution. The first is, have we chosen the best route available for achieving the development end-point that is being aimed at? There may be variations of research route related to final 'design' of end-product, variation of resources that might be used to achieve it, variations of the end-product itself related to how much research is necessary. A technique known as PABLA (Problem Analysis by Logical Approach) has been developed by R. L. Latham over the last ten years [48 and 49] which, although developed for innovatory design, can nevertheless be used in a similar manner for R & D project definition.

The second step is to delineate the plan of the project in some detail. The purpose of this is firstly effectively to formulate the resources and costs and probabilities of success of a chosen project so that we can be quite clear what terms are reasonable to use in cost/benefit calculations. Whilst this book is not the right place for detailed description of the techniques available, a brief description is given of critical path planning, with branched networks, as it can be used in project definition. A description of cost/benefit analysis will then follow, which gives us a mathematical method of calculating the economic gain that might be expected from a given research project and thus supplies us with one criterion for ranking possible projects before ultimate selection.

PABLA

PABLA is a tool for use in planning and manipulating the resources available to attain a stated goal. Correctly applied it becomes a penetrating systematic approach which exposes key problems, expands the search for alternative solution and guides the synthesis and selection of solutions which match the real needs of the problem. As a first step, the data that exist concerning the problem must be examined and requirements which are not postulated must be uncovered. Secondly, the time needs to be satisfied must be determined from the data and requirements. Thirdly, the optimum solution that satisfies the true needs can be produced by manipulating the resources (mental and tangible). Of course it may be argued that these steps are always taken by the experienced researcher. The more formal approach to them which PABLA teaches has been found to pay good dividends. It is particularly applicable to the development type of research project though not without relevance to the earlier research phases.

All problems at any point in the decision-making process can be studied from six angles or facets, each of the six contributing to the job as a whole. Failure to consider one or more of these facets during the planning process is one of the main reasons for inferior solutions.

These facets are:

Achievement: What has to be done

Why has it to be done

What else might be done

What *should* be done

Place: Where is it to be done

Why is it to be done there

Where else might it be done

Where *should* it be done

Time: When has it to be done

Why has it to be done then

When might it be done

When *should* it be done

Resources: What resources are required to do it

Why are those resources required to do it

What other resources might be used to do it

What resources *should* be used to do it.

Method: How is it to be done

Why is it to be done that way

How else might it be done

How *should* it be done

Justification: Why are we doing it

Purposes, causes, consequences

Why *should* it be done

Satisfactory answers to the 'should' questions will be arrived at only by testing alternative ideas. Progressive simplification results from continually asking the following questions:

How can we:

Eliminate, combine, standardise, transfer, modify, simplify. This series is standard method study practice but this thinking is applicable to the design of a development project as much as to design engineering or process operation.

The PABLA method is to complete the four charts shown in Figs. 5.2–5.5. These charts are shown relative to an engineering design job, but it matters little whether the end-point is a design or development package. The principles are the same and in any case the actual questions asked can be modified to suit any particular circumstances.

The essence of Chart 1 is that it provides a well-thought-out statement of the factors that affect the job – a file of the information affecting the job such as what the end product is to be used for, what influences govern its use or its 'installation', and what existing knowledge and resources are available to assist in the project.

Chart 2 seeks to establish what it is we are seeking to do – what is the best end-point.

Chart 3 is perhaps the most important, for it explores all possible means of meeting the objective – the point being that no inhibitions should be allowed to interfere with the free

OPERATIONAL AND ENVIRONMENTAL ASPECTS		C1
USAGE	INFLUENCES	EXISTING RESOURCES
Occasion 1	Environment 2	Previous designs 3
Duration 4	Safety 5	Existing equipment 6
Frequency 7	Policies 8	Services available 9
Sequence 10	Test and install 11	Experience 12
Operators 13	Time scale 14	15
Maintenance 16	Finance 17	18
Personal acceptability 19	Manufacture 20	21

FIG. 5.2 PABLA Chart 1 – Factors which affect the job

statement of the possibilities. As workable ideas emerge they must be explored to test their usability, both in terms of what research knowledge exists and the practicability of success in taking the idea forward.

ENGINEERING DESIGN SPECIFICATION			C2
OBJECTIVE	PERFORMANCE	ASSUMPTIONS	This specification to be read in conjunction with charts nos.
			Effect on environment
			Limitations

FIG. 5.3 PABLA Chart 2 – The best end-point

Methods of fulfilling requirement	Conflicts with	Theoretical	Conflicts with	Practical	Conflicts with	Size and material	Conflicts with	Production Aspects Ind. Mfr. Test, Install, Transport.	Conflicts with	Probable cost research needed	
PRINCIPLES OF SYSTEMS											**C3**
						CONSIDERATIONS					

FIG. 5.4 PABLA Chart 3 – Exploration of possible methods

Chart 4 provides a final review of the chosen optimum solution to ensure that it hangs together in all its parts.

REQUIREMENTS OF SYSTEM FEATURES									C4
Feature									
Function & method of functioning									
Characteristics — Decided									
Characteristics — Undecided									
Decision by — Customer									
Decision by — Project Eng'r									
Decision by — Design Eng'r									
Source of supply — Stores									
Source of supply — Purchase									
Source of supply — Design									
Source of supply — Existing									

FIG. 5.5 PABLA Chart 4 – Final review of optimum system

It cannot be emphasised too much, however, that the majority of the direct benefit from PABLA is derived, not from filling in paper records, but by the mental discipline demanded of the user in the continual questioning of every fact or supposed fact, and the necessity of continually reviewing the perspective in which the best solution stands.

The completion of such charts provides also a valuable record indicating why the project developed in the way it did. The review of an R & D project can then be more soundly based and changes in it more effectively made by up-dating of the charts.

The maximum benefit would appear to be gained on those jobs for which the questions are the most difficult to answer and that is usually where the innovatory content is greatest.

CRITICAL PATH PLANNING AND BRANCHED NETWORKS

If we are going to apply cost/benefit criteria in our choice of research projects it is necessary to have a logical and as precise an expression as possible of the path that the research projects would be expected to follow. This might be called the strategy plan. Such an analysis can be performed in successive degrees of detail depending on the nature of the likely cost/benefit, the size of the project, the degree of complication, etc. Producing a plan in this sense has two principal functions in research management:

(a) Providing a basis for project evaluation, including assessment of resources needed.

(b) Providing a basis for the execution and control of the research itself.

It is more important that the plan of the operation should be correct than that any particular method should be used. Indeed some research workers can hold their entire strategy in their heads, being fully aware of how long different elements in the work will take, when and what are the resource requirements, the effects of success or failure of different experiments on the overall programme and the costs of alternative plans. It is, however, becoming increasingly usual for more formal plan statements to be made so that communication between the scientists and those concerned with project evaluation, resource supply, engineering, financing or with fitting the plan for a particular piece of research into the larger plan of a technological project can be achieved.

By plan here is meant the setting out, in some accepted 'language', of proposed courses of action which summate to the complete project, with the impingement of other courses of action, resource availability, etc.

The simplest form of such a plan is the time-based bar chart, where the sequence of operation is straightforward and the impingement of other activities simple and easily appreciated. Fig. 5.6 shows such a bar chart.

This would not be adequate, however, to show the entire plan of a complicated, long-term research project whose out-

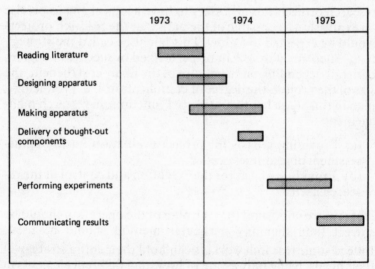

FIG. 5.6 Bar-line chart for simple research project

come was important in time, cost and results, to a major project.

Such planning exercises usually make use of various planning techniques based on the concepts of networks. The technical details for complete understanding of the principles and usage of such networks in the R & D situation are not appropriate to this book. They have been particularly clearly expounded in Beattie and Reader's *Quantitative Management in R and D*, [50] but it may be of value to say what the main types of network are and give some idea of how they can be used in R & D management.

The most usual and simple network concept is the Critical Path Network used where all the major tasks to complete a project are known in advance, the network being used to state how the performance of one task impinges on another and contributes to the completion of the project. Times for the performance of each task may be written into each network.

Such a network is shown in Fig. 5.7. A series of chains of activity will emerge from start to completion of the project. One of these will be the longest on a time basis and is called the critical path because there is no time to spare in this chain of events if the project is to be completed on time. Such a network is known as an arrow diagram, the lines or arrows representing component tasks and the circles or nodes represent points of time when some tasks end and others begin. Each node is numbered for simple reference and the time element placed at each arrow. Sometimes nodes are linked with a 'dummy arrow' implying a link between tasks without any particular operation or time being involved.

The network describes for us the basic strategy of the project, tells us how long it will take and at what points various activities must be joined with each other. The critical path can be calculated and this tells us on which activities control must be most closely exercised.

As the project proceeds actual events will produce the need to up-date the network and it can happen that a new critical path is thus formed to which progressing precedence has to be switched.

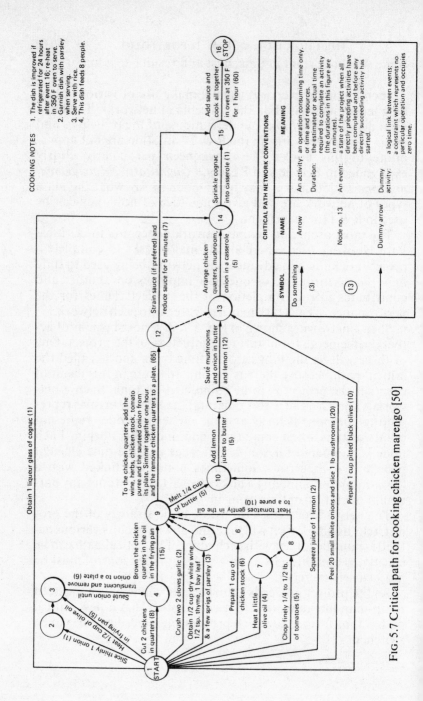

Fig. 5.7 Critical path for cooking chicken marengo [50]

BRANCHING NETWORKS

Usually, with a research project all the major tasks are not known in advance, and the plan has to take into account the effects of failure as well as success and the alternative routes to a project end-point that this entails. Methods of drawing up plans with such eventualities in mind have been attempted by many different workers and one method is a development of the critical path network, known as branching networks, sometimes called probabilistic or stochastic networks.

The term branching is used because at certain nodes there is a branch in the plan indicating that one or more of several different courses of action may then be taken dependent on events arising after the programme has started.

Fig. 5.8 gives a simple case of a network with branches and it will be seen that a new 'node' symbol is used in such a case.

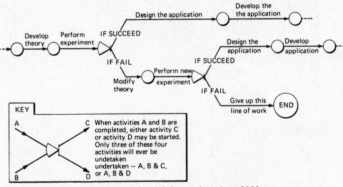

FIG. 5.8 Network with branch points [50]

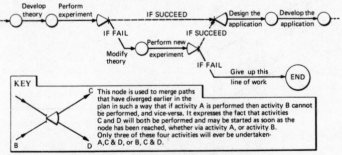

FIG. 5.9 Network with branch points [50]

In Fig. 5.8 the activities 'Design the application' and 'Develop the application' although they involve the same work appear twice on the plan and to avoid this a third type of node

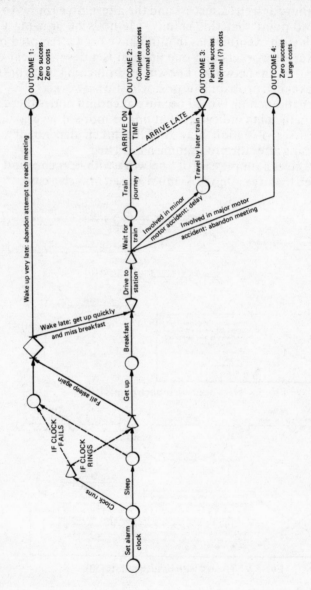

Fig. 5. 10 A network plan: attend morning meeting [50]

may be used to bring together again these same paths (see Fig. 5.9).

There are various extensions and alternatives available for other situations and in this way plans can be drawn up on a branching network basis to describe a project where the outcome of certain activities is in doubt (e.g. Fig. 5.10). This is typical of an R & D project, but also exists in many other complicated projects; for instance, where a decision between two routes might be called for at a certain point in time when a whole body of research activity will have yielded results which will sway a decision in one or another direction.

USES OF NETWORKS

At the project evaluation stage such branching network plans may be made use of in a variety of ways.

1. *Time*   As with critical path planning time elements can be inserted (or best estimates of times) so that the time penalties of different routes to an end-point can be made known and total time estimated.

2. *Probability*   An important element in project selection involving research is the probability of success and this can seldom be quantified on a better basis than an assessment on the basis of experience. This is more difficult to do, however, with a long and complicated project than with one with a relatively small element in it. With a network it is, therefore, possible to assign probabilities to each element of a network and by processes using the mathematics of compounding probabilities, to estimate the overall probability of the project.

3. *Resource allocation*   It can happen that some elements in a plan are dependent on the amount of a given resource available, e.g. machine tools. If such an element does not occur at a critical point the resource allocation may be small, but if it is critical it may be necessary to increase the resource at that point in the plan. This also applies to the allocation of staff, and obviously where an important research result greatly affects the subsequent conduct of a project the staff might be increased at that point if an increase in staff might hasten the result.

4. *Cost estimates*   The plan can also be used to help in the estimation of costs. The resources required and the time spent at each link in chain, when added together, will give the total project costs.

Equally, if alternative routes to the same end are available, a simple plan drawn up for each route might quickly tell us which route is the less costly. Project plans drawn with experience can particularly help in avoiding underestimating which is a considerable problem in R & D work, frequently caused by the lack of study of all the implications in the project.

In the evaluation of a potential project it is important that the aims or potential end-points or consequences are written into the strategy plan. Then the calculation of benefits that could arise is more easily undertaken and the strategy plan will make a significant contribution to a cost/benefit study.

COST BENEFIT ANALYSIS (CBA)

We have seen how potential R & D projects are assembled and how critical path networks can be used to establish the programme and essential parameters of any given project, with one of the important uses being to enable the expected cost of a project to be evaluated.

At this stage it is possible to use the techniques of cost benefit analysis to help us further in the choice of the most useful projects. [51 and 52]

CBA involves a systematic comparison between the *cost* of carrying out an activity or service and the *value* of that activity or service, quantified as far as possible – all costs and benefits being taken into account. While used as a technique for administrative decision making, particularly for major capital investment projects for many years, it has only relatively recently been used in the context of R & D projects and progress has been slow relative to its use elsewhere. A Programmes Analysis Unit, originally a joint unit of the Ministry of Technology and the UKAEA was set up at Chilton, Berkshire in 1967 and many developments in the use of CBA for the selection of research and development programmes, particularly those funded by government, are now emanating from there.

CBA involves the listing and consideration of as many effects as can be identified – beneficial and adverse, short-term and long-term, tangible and intangible – on all persons and groups likely to be affected (however remotely), as against the listing and consideration of all the costs, monetary or otherwise which go into performing the activity. In so far as these can be evaluated on a common scale (monetary if possible), the ratio of the two (the benefit/cost ratio) gives a measure of the desirability of undertaking the activity and there will be a strong case for preferring the project which shows the higher benefit/cost ratio.

As well as presenting a comparison between two or more alternative courses of action, CBA can also assist decision makers by reducing to financial or statistical terms as many consequences as possible, so removing unsupported opinions, focusing attention on whether known but unmeasurable benefits appear to be sufficient to justify the measurable costs they involve, and it can be used continually to reassess a project in the light of historical evidence of its costs and emerging consequences.

The value of CBA is largely dependent on how completely all costs can be anticipated and estimated and how thoroughly the effects can be predicted and quantified. In this lie some of the reasons for the difficulty of applying the technique to R & D. The first major uncertainty arises because it is in the nature of research that we cannot guarantee that it will attain a given objective or how much it will cost to get there. The nearer the research is to basic or exploratory the less precise can these estimates be, but nevertheless after the exploratory work has been done – which is when we are most concerned about putting the greater sums of money into R & D – estimates of cost of R & D can be reasonably made.

To deal with this problem the concept of 'probability' of technical success of the research, P_t, is introduced. This is a subjective judgement made by experts in the field and techniques are available to improve on the simple evaluation by a single expert. We have also seen how network analysis can be used in such a way that 'probability' factors can be built up.

It may transpire that the R & D will only achieve partial attainment of the objective or that it will take longer to do than was anticipated. Either will need a re-examination of the costs and benefits in relation to the market.

The second major uncertainty arises from the fact that a successful R & D project needs to be followed by 'exploitation' and there are many obstacles to the successful achievement of such 'coupling' or 'diffusion'. An example is a programme of work on uranium ore processing at AWRE Aldermaston which was highly successful technically in establishing a number of advances in the technology, in accordance with the parameters fed into a cost/benefit analysis. Unfortunately, the world market in uranium had slowed up because international anticipation of nuclear power expansion had not been realised, so the benefits of the research will be at least seriously delayed.

These market considerations are extremely important to the successful outcome of an R & D project and it is important that 'marketability of the likely product' (in the widest sense of the phrase) is continually re-examined along with the progress of the research itself.

This problem is similarly dealt with using a probability factor, P_c. As we have seen in Chapter 1, research and development is one element in a spectrum starting with exploratory or even basic research and proceeding through R & D, plant or prototype production and sales exploitation, before it begins to pay off. This is for a relatively simple project where the benefit will arise in direct money terms and in such cases general figures for the ratio of research:development;capital investment of 5:15:80 have been quoted. Of course, sometimes research does not exist in such a simple cycle – capital investment may not be involved at all, as where the benefit comes from licensing a process, or where the objective of the research is to reduce capital expenditure by developing a process which simply gets a greater product output from a given plant.

In all cases, however, it is important that it should be clear whether we are estimating the benefit from the whole cycle of activities or whether only on the R & D contribution – and the costs need to correspond.

For the purpose of using benefit/cost ratios for ranking purposes, or for helping to decide on a preferred choice of project from a number of alternatives, we may use, in a straightforward case, the simple formula

$$\text{Benefit/cost ratio} = \frac{P_t \times P_c(p - c) \times V \times L}{\text{Total costs (R \& D + exploitation)}}$$

Where
P_t = 'probability' of technical success
P_c = 'probability' of commercial success
p = price
c = cost
V = annual sales volume
L = life of product

$$\text{or Benefit/cost ratio} = \frac{P_t \times P_c \times \dfrac{I_1}{1 + r} + \dfrac{I_2}{(1 + r)^2} + \cdots \dfrac{I_n}{(1 + r)^n}}{\text{Total discounted R \& D etc., costs}}$$

Where
r = discounted rate
I_n = net income in year n

More complicated formulae taking into account the possibility of projects being terminated before benefits begin to come through can be developed such as

$$\frac{\text{Expectance of total benefit}}{\text{Expectance of total cost}} = \frac{P_R P_P P_M \overline{(I(r))} - \overline{C(r)}}{\overline{R(r)} + P_R P \overline{D(r)} + P_R P_D \overline{M(r)} + P_R D_R M_R \overline{F(r)}}$$

Where P_R, P_D, P_M are probabilities of success at research, development and marketing respectively

$\overline{I(r)}$ summated expected income discounted

$\overline{C(r)}$ summated expected production costs discounted

$\overline{R(r)}, \overline{D(r)}, \overline{M(r)}$ discounted costs of research, development and marketing

$\overline{F(r)}$ discounted value of investment necessary after marketing success has been achieved.

Cost/benefit analysis in relation to R & D is frequently allied with other techniques derived from management sciences such as systems analysis, modelling, operations research and decision analysis in order to determine the proper objectives and to work out completely the implications of the objectives to obtain the full record of the costs.

The degree of complication that enters into the calculation is determined by the nature of the project and its ramifications. If we are assessing the implications of developing desalination processes, for instance, we are clearly concerned with world markets and world-wide social corollaries. If we are assessing which of several potential new minor chemicals might be the best to invest short term R & D in, a less complicated approach will suffice. The actual value of the benefit/cost ratio is also pertinent. Because of the uncertainties of research and the resources it will use, not only do we build appropriate factors into the calculation but high values of the ratio are demanded – at least 3:1 or 5:1 before resources are committed. But equally it follows that if ratios are very high, refined calculations are unnecessary and resources will be committed more on the basis of probability of research success than carefully compared benefit/cost ratios.

The exercise of undertaking cost/benefit analyses, despite all the difficulties that are involved in the R & D context, and in addition to providing a mathematical means of project selection, gives rise to other advantages, for example:

(a) It leads to careful questioning and identification of goals.

(b) It assists in decisions on justifiable levels of R & D investment.

(c) It points to the importance of timing in relation to project viability.

(d) It discloses areas of indeterminacy which may justify further exploratory attack before resources are fully committed.

CHOICE OF RESEARCH PROJECT – APPRAISAL GRAPHS

We have seen that many factors go into the choice of research projects, some dependent on the environment conditioned by the parent authority, some, by no means least, on the semi-mathematically calculated gain factor to be expected. To systematise the choice under these difficult circumstances it is sometimes useful to use appraisal graphs of the type shown in Fig. 5.11. The factors most relevant to a given laboratory programme would be used. They provide a first step towards a quantitative method for rating projects taking all important factors into account; they tend to eliminate some bias and to furnish a degree of consistency. By up-dating them at regular intervals they can also be used as a useful control tool.

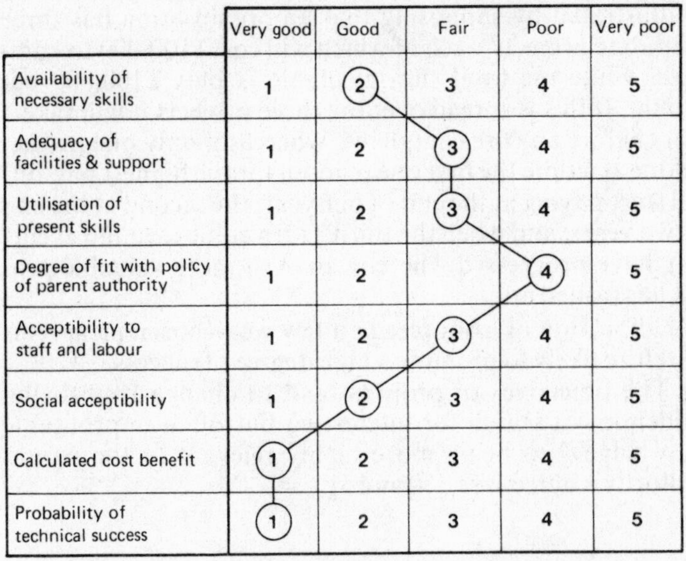

	Very good	Good	Fair	Poor	Very poor
Availability of necessary skills	1	(2)	3	4	5
Adequacy of facilities & support	1	2	(3)	4	5
Utilisation of present skills	1	2	(3)	4	5
Degree of fit with policy of parent authority	1	2	3	(4)	5
Acceptibility to staff and labour	1	2	(3)	4	5
Social acceptibility	1	(2)	3	4	5
Calculated cost benefit	(1)	2	3	4	5
Probability of technical success	(1)	2	3	4	5

FIG. 5.11 Appraisal graph for ranking research projects

BENEFITS OF USING FORMAL PROJECT REVIEW

Clearly a good deal of effort can go into the review of candidate research projects and their eventual selection to form the research portfolio of the research department. While the advantages of using the different techniques have been indicated, it will be of interest to mention the advantages that are claimed overall for the use of some or all of these formal project review systems.

(a) Research management is made more aware of the comparative pay-off to be expected from candidate projects and as a result many projects might not be entered on, which would hitherto have been considered as good.

(b) More resources tend to be allocated to fewer projects. There is a natural tendency in research departments to spread resources thinly over many projects in order to keep up with developments on all fronts. There are advantages, however, in taking on as few projects as possible. This may be illustrated by supposing that an organisation has three candidate projects, each of which will cost £100,000 to complete, while the total sum available is only £100,000 per annum. If this is spread over the three projects it will take 3 years before any are completed, whereas if only one project is done at a time the first one (chosen for the highest pay-off) will start paying at the end of one year, the second at the end of two years, and when the third's turn comes around events may have progressed whereby an even more valuable project has turned up.

The allocation of resources to a few well-chosen projects is therefore likely to promote a high degree of success.

(c) The objectives of projects tend to change from being academic – a search for interesting but often unprofitable knowledge – to being more highly relevant to the parent authority's objectives. [50 and 5]

DEFINING PROJECT TO 'CUSTOMER' REQUIREMENTS

We have seen how research projects are chosen in many different strategic situations. If critical path planning has been used to formulate the nature of the project we shall already have thought carefully over the substance of the research in relation to the 'customer' or project requirement. It is, however, dangerous to rush into the actual research activity without careful planning, firstly to be satisfied that the right questions are being asked of the researcher so that they are in a form in which they can be dealt with as a research activity, and so that the answers, if successful, can be used to solve the 'customer' problem; secondly, to establish in detail the resources that are required, when they can be available in relation to when they are needed, and so arranging all the staff and other facilities as necessary.

Two plans, therefore, need to be drawn up:

(A) The Customer's plan by which the proposed programme of activities and how they should lead to the anticipated endpoint are succinctly described.

It is immensely important to a research organisation that the proposal of a research programme to a 'customer' should be clearly made so that potential sponsors can consider all the important factors without being 'blinded by science'. It must, of course, be obvious that research programmes cannot be guaranteed to produce satisfaction and this should be clearly understood. The writing of proposals for potential sponsors should not be taken casually nor regarded as unimportant. A proposal should be grammatically correct, easy to read and contain the description of a logical research programme together with a clear statement of what is being aimed at. A skilfully prepared proposal will have the following features:

1. It will completely describe the programme and the ideas on which the research is based. It should be in terms which are no more technical than necessary to put the project over.
2. It will not contain extraneous material, but will be concise and to the point.
3. It will be clear in meaning, using easily understood English and will have a format which although correct is well organised. It will be easy to read.
4. It will be as technically correct as possible, bearing in mind the simplification necessary.
5. Its tone will be appropriate so that false enthusiasms are not created. [53]

In a large organisation where research proposals are a common occurrence, consideration should be given to employing a special writer for them.

Presentation If a research proposal is considerable in size and novel in nature it is advisable that a documentary proposal should be followed by a personal presentation. This may take the form of a simple meeting in which the document is gone through to elucidate concepts and eliminate misunderstandings and doubts, or it may be in the form of a series of short talks with appropriate visual aids followed by a question and answer session. Such a presentation can alert all the interested parties in a sponsoring organisation to the significance of the proposal and provide a great help to the senior management of the sponsors in understanding the proposal and formulating their decision.

(B) The Contractor's plan is a more detailed statement, probably in network form of the objectives, operational stages, resource inputs and end-points of the research proposal.

In this way there is less likely to be any misunderstanding between the contractor and the customer about what research is planned towards what objective and the research has a better chance of being conducted efficiently, expeditiously and economically.

From time to time, arising from what happens during the research phase or what happens to the objective set by the customer, a change of programme may become necessary. Wherever there is a substantial change of direction so caused, the customer plan should be restated and agreed with him and then the contractor's plan should be correspondingly modified.

This whole procedure is strongly to be recommended, however non-project-orientated the research is to be, because all research fits into the same overall pattern, being strategically planned for a 'customer'; all research is more expeditiously carried out if required resources are brought to bear at the right time, and all research workers are the better for thinking carefully of what they intend to do before they start their research.

Further, such plans if correctly distributed enable any department providing an input to the research – information services, design services, engineering services, glass-blowing, analytical services, personnel department, financial department – to plan *their* activities so that the services are available when required.

TOTAL EXPENDITURE ON RESEARCH

Choosing a portfolio of selected R & D topics must of course be done within the circumscribing factor of total allowable expenditure. More will be said about this in the section on budgeting (p. 170) but a guide to this in an established organisation can be obtained by drawing up curves of the type shown in Fig. 5.12. Research has to produce new products to satisfy the market which will arise when old products are no longer saleable, and it has to provide products for whatever growth is en-

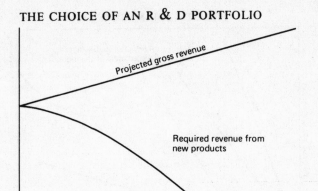

FIG. 5.12 Basis for assessing total R & D expenditure

visaged (this may be negative, as in government defence spending). Such a pattern is of universal application in principle although quantifying it may not be easy other than in certain industrial contexts. It is, however, the type of exercise that should be performed relative to the selection of a portfolio if the total expenditure is to be rationally estimated against parent authority needs.

TIMING OF RESEARCH PROGRAMMES

The importance of relating research to 'market' requirements is continually emphasised in this book and in no respect is this more important than in respect of timing. It is necessary to time the end-point of an R & D project so that technological achievement will occur at the point of optimum market potential, but this is one of the most important and difficult aspects of long-term planning. Fig. 5.13 shows the type of situation we are faced with. A new product or process has a certain time area of acceptability and different research programmes will produce a result at different times. The plan must be chosen (plan X or plan Y) where it will reach fruition just when

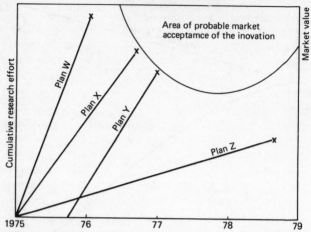

FIG. 5.13 Choosing the research plan in relation to the 'market'

market demand is accelerating and the research programme must be started at the latest date possible so that a maximum of information will be available.

Plan *W* is completed too early in that it has probably cost too much by being performed before the last information was available. Plan *Z* has missed the market altogether although it has cost the least.

CHANGING THE PORTFOLIO – STOPPING PROJECTS

So far, in this chapter, we have considered the steps necessary to establish a portfolio of research programmes and then to plan them – in fact the steps necessary before any research actually starts.

Before proceeding to the next stage of considering how to control R & D projects once they have started, we might examine the problems of changing a portfolio and of stopping projects within it.

Earlier, the necessity of reviewing the project plan in the light of research results or deviations in the customer's objectives has been discussed. In most cases this will not lead to a change in the portfolio of projects. But if the nature of the research results is dramatically off-beam relative to the objective (it may be a totally unanticipated failure or success, a lead to an entirely new and more worthwhile objective, a significant snag which may necessitate an increase in the time scale of the programme), it may result in the necessity for changing the entire nature of the project or make it desirable to close it down altogether.

Similarly a change in the situation of the 'customer' – market research may indicate that the objective has become untimely, one's 'competitor' (whether in defence, industry, medicine or whatever) may have produced a result which makes it necessary to advance the objective – may mean that the current project is useless and it either has to be modified, replaced or stopped.

There are many reasons for project abandonment in practice, the most common being a failure to conduct an adequate 'market assessment' before starting R & D, although projects are seldom shelved for single non-technical reasons.

Factors may be broadly classified as:

(a) The price might be too high, either of the research or the product it is leading to, adequately and economically to fulfil the 'market' requirement. This may not be apparent until a substantial amount of research has been done.

(b) Uncertainty whether the 'market' would welcome a new product – particularly if dominated by a single 'buyer'. Again a substantial amount of research may have to be carried out before the nature of the 'product' and its pay-off is known. It may not turn out to be as saleable as was hoped for.

(c) Lack of marketing resources or production capacity. As the research results emerge, it may transpire that the end-product is likely to require a different distribution network or different type of production plant from that associated with the normal operations of the parent organisation, and it might rightly be decided that the research should be terminated rather than for the present organisation to set up new production plant or explore new distribution methods. It does not follow that the research has been wasted, as it may be possible to make licensing or other commercial arrangements (perhaps through the NRDC), or to exploit the research knowledge as it stands, through an external organisation.

(d) Shortage of R & D resources. This might arise from the loss of key staff, the emergence of new, higher priority projects or changes in the facilities available to the research department. Such considerations might lead to operating the research programme on a new extended time scale or temporary abandonment, rather than complete stoppage. In such a case a revised plan should be drawn up and its consequences made known to the customer.

For these reasons, or others, the portfolio of research projects will be under continual review, with some projects changing direction or time scale, some being allowed to persist in spite of diminishing value and some being terminated altogether.

The termination of research projects is one of the most difficult of a director's activities. Among the reasons for unjustifiably prolonged continuance are:

(a) Over-optimism and the hope that although the research is going badly, some turn for the better will occur, or hesitancy of the researcher to report failure.

(b) Reluctance of staff to change their project unless a more promising one appears within their own field. (In fact research staff are more flexible than they themselves appreciate, and if persuaded into a new field can often operate very effectively indeed – the more so because they are bringing new methods of thinking and techniques where they may not have been hitherto applied.)

(c) Administrative delay in reassigning personnel.

(d) Necessity of proving conclusively that success is not possible.

(e) Top management bias in favour of a project.

(f) Sheer momentum of a project, especially if it is a large one.

(g) Elusive or vague definition of the objectives of the project.

(h) Desire to pursue off-shoots and tangential directions.

While all the above reasons need carefully to be guarded

against, it is sometimes desirable to allow a project to run on beyond the time when really paying results are being obtained, as when a particular expertise or team might be kept going, waiting for an emerging new project for which they are particularly suited or simply because it is desirable to keep a team in existence in relation to the general nature of the laboratory and its likely future commitments. This is particularly so if results appear to be interesting in directions other than required by the research project. It is even better to find the team a project which does use them in a 'cost-effective' way, but this is by no means always a reasonable possibility.

When a project has, however, reached the end of its useful life and there is no justifiable reason for its continuance, the problem should be faced squarely and the project wound up. For too many researches are allowed to carry on in universities, government laboratories and industrial laboratories although they are long past yielding any really worthwhile results. The best way to wind it up is to find a new project which has a sound cost/benefit ratio, is challenging technically although soluble, and makes substantial use of the team concerned within the context of the particular laboratory. This is to start again on the process of project selection in an efficient way.

On the other hand care must be taken not to terminate a project too early. This can happen where the more interesting scientific aspects have reached a successful end-point and the scientists tend to find it boring to carry out those researches which are going to confirm viability beyond doubt, explore the appropriate limits of practical application, or carry out the fringe investigations to provide data for appropriate exploitation. Many new ideas fail to reach successful exploitation because prototypes or pilot plants run into insurmountable problems because the research behind them has not been sufficiently complete. It may be necessary for the director to arrange for a more development-minded team to take over from the more scientifically-motivated team, but somehow the research must continue until adequate information is available before it is terminated.

It will be seen that the termination of projects needs almost as much care, skill and judgement as their selection.

TECHNOLOGY ASSESSMENT

In recent years much concern has been expressed about the ill effects which advancing technology can produce – pollution of the environment, noise, effluent disposal, wasting of limited resources and harmful side effects, being phrases with which we are daily bombarded. A reaction of the technologists has been quickly to take these matters into closer consideration, along with the advantages of technological advance. The concept of technology assessment has, therefore, been developed which may be defined as the systematic study of the effects on society that may occur when a technology is introduced, extended or modified, with special emphasis on the impacts that are unintended, indirect and delayed. In other words, technology assessment aims to look beyond the simple cost effectiveness of new technology, in an attempt to recognise as many potential side effects as possible: the social accounting of technological change.

This means the desirability of associating social scientists, economists and even lawyers with researchers at quite early stages in project selection to give value and weight to social disbenefits when the choice occurs. At any rate the setting out of research programmes should always include those elements whose function is to ensure that the technology becomes socially acceptable. Methods of dealing with wastes arising, study of possible side effects, the effect of reactants and products on manufacturing workers and the environment of their use must form part of the total R & D programme at least where careful thought can recognise them. [54]

The choice of an R & D portfolio can thus be seen to be a very complicated problem demanding skill, knowledge, judgement, a feel for the abilities and likely success of the research teams, an economic sense and sympathy with the motivations of research workers and managers. If there is a tendency for it to be technique-orientated this must be striven against. Techniques, to be used successfully, must be regarded as tools, and decisions reached only with an understanding of the system as a whole – the research department and the parent authority on whose behalf it is working. In practice it is probably not quite so complicated as it may seem, because firstly, much of any R

& D programme is dictated by the obvious needs of the parent organisation, and secondly, research programmes are built up over many years with choice and change only affecting minor fractions of the total activity each year.

Nevertheless, it probably represents the most important activity of the director in most research departments, one to be thought over and, if necessary, fought over until a well-balanced, telling programme with a high success potential is reached.

SUMMARY

The choice of the R & D portfolio which will best suit the goals of the parent authority is probably the most important task of research management. Three basic situations exist: (a) where the objective has been decided and R & D is one of the tools for carrying it out; (b) where the objective is known in a general way but the research topics to support it have not been uncovered; (c) where the objective is not known in terms of possible research lines. For (b) and (c) in particular it is important to set up consulative arrangements and brainstorming sessions among other techniques to parade research ideas relevant to the overall objectives.

Considerations that go into the final choice of a portfolio are of three types:

(a) arising from the question of how best to use the research resources available;
(b) arising from the needs of the parent authority such as the use of existing production facilities and the will to diversify;
(c) satisfying criteria of giving maximum economic benefit.

Techniques which help us to arrive at calculation of economic benefit are:

(a) Problem analysis by logical approach (PABLA)
(b) Critical path planning with branched networks – which tell us the true nature of the research proposal and enable reasonable assessments to be made of time elements, proba-

bility of success and resources necessary. These are an important basis for calculating

(c) Cost benefit analysis (CBA) – for which calculation formulae are quoted

(d) Project appraisal graphs – which attempt to give some mathematical expression to all these factors.

The advantages of using such formal selection techniques are a greater awareness of comparative pay-off, a more rigorous selection of fewer promising topics and finally an impetus to look carefully for fully relevant topics.

It is desirable, having selected a portfolio on these lines, to take care over preparation of a submission to the 'customer' and methods are suggested for this.

An approach to estimating the total sum to be spent on R & D in relation to the organisation's 'products' is made, with a note on the influence of timing of the research programme on the 'market'.

The difficult problem of closing down projects, in relation to the right end-point to reach for maximum impact on the practicality of the product, the best administrative reasons and finally avoidance of continuance of 'unprofitable' research, is seen to be an important factor of research management.

The present-day impact of technological assessment – relating technology to the problems of society – lead to attention being given to widening research portfolios to ensure that social disadvantages are minimised.

6 Control of R & D projects

GENERAL MANAGEMENT ROLE

Previous chapters have largely dealt with the problem of establishing the right research programmes for an R & D establishment – in relation to the scientific operations in the country as a whole and in relation to different types of organisation and objective. All these activities are very much the concern of research management but the next phase of activity of an R & D department is to carry out the R & D which has been decided upon and a successful role for the manager in this is more difficult to achieve. It has become a cliché that the last thing a director of research does is to direct research, and as with most paradoxical sayings it contains some truth but not the whole truth. For it is also true that in research and in development, more important than techniques of control, useful though they are, is the necessity of the scientific and technical quality of the work to be as high as possible and the director has a prime duty in this to establish appropriate standards. So far as possible, it is desirable that this should be done on a personal basis between the director and the research section leaders in discussing the research projects, but with large multi-layer research organisations, this quickly gets impossible at the higher levels so that the lower directing levels have a particularly difficult role to play in establishing the work standards, as well as linking with the control requirements of higher direction which can no longer be in close touch with the research work itself. The tendency for a manager to become simply a link in a management train under these circumstances needs to be resisted, as indeed needs to be resisted the tendency for all managers to become operators of management techniques, to the exclusion of knowing or caring about the nature of and quality of the research being carried out in the department.

Management techniques do have a very important though secondary role to play in R & D direction and the discussion of some of these is the main preoccupation of this chapter. In general, however, they are tools to be used either by specialists or the research manager while their results, fed to directing level, enable an overall maintenance of communications to be kept up and therefore a general control exercised to ensure that the work continues in accordance with the general strategy of the department.

The three key elements in 'successful' R & D are:

1. An identified need for some R & D effort.
2. The skills and resources to accomplish that effort.
3. The availability of funds to support the effort.

The coupling and integration of these three are the function of management controls, but controls should be an encouraging, helpful, dynamic instrument not an interference or a punishment for digression.

PLACE OF RESEARCH MANAGEMENT IN
MANAGEMENT HIERARCHY

This co-ordinating function has to be effected both within the confines of each project and also, continually, between the research activity and the top parent authority management. A breakthrough on an R & D project sometimes happens unexpectedly and quick action is required for product development and engineering and, in some cases, market development and financial support has to be given quickly. For these reasons R & D management, with its ultimate control of research projects, must assume a relatively high position in the overall organisational framework. This is true in private industry where there should be some research representation at board level, or in wider organisations such as government departments or boards where the research activities should be represented at the highest levels also.

In a study of 117 American firms (in 1964) ranging in size from 25 technical personnel to 400, Seiler [15] analysed the reporting levels for top R & D management to be:

Board of directors	6.4%
President	50.5%
Vice-President	29.6%
Other	3.7%

Another reason why research-minded people should be concerned in the ultimate control of research projects lies in the nature of the life cycle of research. This may be illustrated as in Fig. 6.1. A project may pass through many disappointing periods and hit serious snags, but it requires calm and systematic pacing, with a background of scientific experience to guard against over-enthusiasm and over-pessimism and to judge continuously its likely eventual success. It is the senior research management which will possess this judgement which needs to be communicated at the top decision-making levels.

Even the truth about technical difficulties and problem areas requires expert judgement. Researchers should be encouraged to reveal such problems but some will tend to underplay them and others will lean over backwards to divulge them all. The senior research manager must judge whether they will be overcome or whether they are so severe that the project should be terminated.

BUDGETING AND COST CONTROL

As with most operations the primary means of control is the financial one and although this book is not a suitable place to describe financial control techniques, particular features of budgeting and cost control as related especially to research and development are appropriate. There are very few organisations of any size that do not work to some form of budget and R & D organisations can hardly escape this necessity, spending as they do, large sums of money which make them substantial contributors to the budgets of their parent organisations.

While accepting the necessity of some form of budgeting, however, we must be alive to the difference between research organisations and normal production or service organisations.

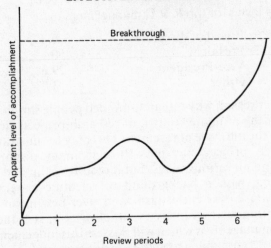

FIG. 6.1 Life cycle of a research project

The difference arises from two elements of research working. The first is that rapid change of direction and purpose is of the essence of fruitful R & D: this does not mean that violent fluctuations will occur in programmes all the time but that research dictates its own future and deviations from the supposed plan must be imaginatively catered for. Secondly, research programmes depend entirely on the men or women carrying them out and all equipment and facilities are there to serve the scientists while with normal large-scale production operations it is usually the plan and machinery which are the main means of effecting the purposes of the organisation. These factors lead to the desirability of flexibility in budgeting which should also take into account such factors as allowing researchers some freedom to spend part of their time and budget on individual research, and bearing in mind that laboratory facilities not only affect the programme of research that can be conducted, but also attract the quality of staff which they deserve.

Another feature of research working which affects budgets is that for a given type of research activity operating budgets are largely controlled by the number of scientists employed. Over half of any operating budget is likely to be attributable to salaries and much of the remainder, such as that for materials, analytical services and administrative services will be proportional to the staff. Differences will exist between different types of research activity as indicated in Chapter 2: for instance, heavy engineering research is likely to require relatively more assistants, instrumentation and engineering services, compared with chemical research, but for a given laboratory these ratios remain fairly constant. It follows that it is more important to budget in terms of professional scientists in relation to the programmes they are to carry out than it is to budget in money terms.

It also follows that substantial sudden changes in operating budgets are difficult to make without equally substantial and sudden changes in the numbers of professional staff. Sudden reductions are bad for morale and also weaken a laboratory because the best people tend to leave first: sudden increases mean rapid recruitment which is difficult to achieve and still produce a good quality team well balanced in age and expertise.

Capital budgets are more nearly conditioned by similar forces to those for other types of operation although the nature of the return on them may be less easily quantifiable.

So we conclude that budgeting for R & D establishments should be flexible to meet changes of orientation, light in control to allow some freedom of choice to scientists, as generous as possible in relation to those facilities which enhance the scientific value and prestige of the work, and with personnel budgeting being closely related to financial. However, some budgeting will need to be accepted so we must consider how it is to be operated. How a budget is arrived at will largely depend on the budgeting methods of the parent or external organisation from which it derives its funds, but it is unlikely to self-generate sufficient funds for its purposes and therefore will require a grant.

In practice it is unlikely that a budget will be constructed for a major expenditure without some reference to what has happened in the past and modifications to the previous budget are the basis of most budget formations. But in theory there are three methods of deriving a budget.

In the first, an analytical method, the parent organisation will decide that a certain sum can be devoted to R & D purposes and the relevant director will produce a programme of work, breaking down the sum into various categories of expenditure after discussion of the options available to him. He may or may not be invited to submit his programme to a higher authority.

At the other extreme is the synthetic process, which particularly applies where the objective of the research is so important that it must be pushed forward as rapidly as possible. In this all the required elements in the programme are assembled, costed, and the total presented to the authorising body. This sort of approach, in a pure form, is probably only applied where a government is operating under severe pressure, as in war-time conditions; money is not in such cases so important as the availability of scientific and ancilliary staff, together with the capacity for providing special facilities.

The third, and by far the most usual method is a combination of the analytic and synthetic approach. The larger part of the programme portfolio is within a reasonably constant sum, fixed by previous experience and slightly modified up or down depending on changing policy as it affects different elements in the portfolio. But new and more substantial projects of considerable importance to the parent organisation might sometimes arise which require a synthetic budget approach, with substantial new capital facilities and an enlargement of staff and services. This part of the portfolio is likely to be adjudged separately by the parent organisation.

In the design of budgeting arrangements it is important to consider the levels of expenditure control. On the one hand it can be argued that scientists should be trained to accept a responsibility for the financial affairs of their work; on the other, that to distract a scientist from the pursuit of his scientific work is wasteful. No doubt some form of compromise is the best solution. More junior scientists with small teams whose expenditure is largely dictated by the requirements of more senior officers can scarcely benefit the system or themselves by the necessity of controlling a budget. But where a scientist has control of a sizeable team of junior scientists and ancilliary staff and makes use of expensive facilities and services, the necessity of controlling a budget is a good discipline leading to a better understanding between working and administrative centres. Undoubtedly, however, the usefulness of budgets declines as it moves downwards through an organisational structure and hardly exists as it reaches the individual researcher.

It is important, however, at whatever level the delegation is practised that a man should only be expected to control a budget if he can control the elements that give rise to the expenditure of the budget. A budget should, therefore, not include overheads and services which will be charged irrespective of the care with which the budget is managed, for this would only lead to frustration and apathy. It is also important that similar conditions apply to capital as to operating budgets. We should avoid a situation where a man has an operating budget of perhaps £100,000 a year and can manipulate men and services within that figure, but needs to go to much higher authority to spend £100 on a capital item. Indeed, the concept of a capital item needs to be interpreted with flexibility in a research laboratory. For often a large machine with expensive instrumental and control appendages will be designed by a scientist/engineer team for an experimental purpose of short duration and at the end it will be worth nothing. So it is a sound rule that capital budgeting should be reserved for machines of a durable character – say with a life of five years or more and which will retain a separate identity throughout their life.

STEPS IN PREPARATION OF BUDGET

There will be many ways in which budgets are drawn up, with varying contributions by the scientists, managers, scientific directors, financial executives, planning departments and parent boards but a typical series of steps might be as follows:

1. The research director reviews the forward programme with his senior research management staff and, with the assistance of a planning group (if the organisation has one) draws up the budget for each project or group of projects, depending on their size, in respect of manpower, services and capital requirements, and thus advances a tentative budget.

2. This will be discussed with the senior research management and changes made in so far as the director is convinced by the arguments of his research managers. The budget is reformulated in financial terms by a planning or financial departments, breaking it down into materials, services, pay, etc. and building it up with overheads and other ancilliary charges. In this way a document in the required format is drawn up for presentation to the parent authority.

3. This will be examined by the parent authority who will suggest changes in line with higher financial or technical policy. The research director has at this point to decide whether to fight the changes or accept them.

4. After reconciliation, a formal budget statement will be drawn up by co-operation between the director and the financial or planning department, accompanied by a simple, although meaningful, statement of the research objective and plan.

5. Depending on the size and complexity of the research organisation, the budget statement will be broken down into sectional areas or tasks which may correspond to projects or to centres of budget control such as senior scientists. This is so that those who have a financial control responsibility know what their targets are. These areas or tasks should be sufficiently large to be worth the effort involved both in producing the budget and in exercising control through it subsequently.

TOTAL BUDGET

There are no known relationships between optimum R & D expenditures and another single variable or group of variables which can be used to establish the research budget with a reliable degree of accuracy.

In the case of organisations which exist mainly for profit making a curve of the type shown in Fig. 5.12 will give some guide. Commercial concerns may also compute ratios between total R & D costs and either (1) profits, (2) competitors spend, (3) total sales, or (4) the firm's share of the market, and may well conclude that they should not be too far out of line on any of these criteria. What is certain is that in any lively research organisation there is likely to be a continual pressure for upward revision of the total budget.

In organisations like those financed by government departments, especially where simply defined 'profit' cannot be calculated, the problem is much more difficult and the necessity of having sound reasons for conducting any research becomes more important. These may not be economic reasons but they should appear to have some social need.

Thus the budgeting determination by top line officials is a matter of using broad gauges to see if the budget requests of research officers are reasonable.

LIMITATIONS OF A BUDGET AS A CONTROL

It is wise to realise that the periodic budget is a primary financial tool for the control of certain aspects of R & D. In no way can it be considered a technical control, and even as a basic financial control it has several distinct limitations. It is useful in controlling the total funds to be spent, ensuring to a limited extent that resources are used on projects approved by the management, but there is no foolproof method by which budgeting amounts and actual expenditures can be matched and the resulting variances interpreted as a measure of success or lack of success in R & D activity. Percentage expenditure is not a measure of percentage completion. Research results which can be produced with a specified amount of funds cannot be predicted with a sufficient certainty to make budgeting controls as effective as they are for most other industrial type activities.

As we move from basic, through mission-orientated research, to development, however, the budgeting tool becomes more useful.

The difficulty encountered in interpreting an R & D budgeting variance may be illustrated by the fact that if a project is running substantially under budget, this may indicate that the project is moving along at a much more rapid rate than had been expected or, conversely that difficulties are slowing it up. It may, therefore, be in front of or behind the projected target date and this again can be for scientific reasons, or because management has not apportioned the right resources. Using budgeting as a control is useful if it detects the wrong apportionment of resources, but quite inadequate to test whether the project is proceeding satisfactorily scientifically.

FREQUENCY OF BUDGET PREPARATION AND REVIEW

It is likely that the timing of budget preparation will conform to that for the parent authority and it is likely to be produced annually, with perhaps a review at quarterly or half-yearly intervals. It is also very desirable in research establishments that there should be something like a five-year budget estimate also, which, although not produced with the same precision, will guide the general conduct of a laboratory in relation to staff, general facilities and services.

Flexibility is however of great importance, and the foremost problems caused by inflexibility of budgeting allocations include:

(a) Failure of budget plans to keep pace with project developments so that new project requests and budget revisions are not acted upon quickly enough in relation to research progress.

(b) A tendency for the R & D groups to concentrate only on a conservative approach to solving research problems.

(c) Reducing the likelihood of projects being updated in relation to changing parent authority objectives.

(d) The unrestrained spending of surplus funds either at the end of a project or at the year's end.

Budgets should, therefore, be reviewed periodically at such a level that changes in projects or the budget for projects can be effected.

SOURCE OF BUDGET

In any organisation, the source of the budget needs careful consideration. To put it at its simplest, if the production department's budget carries the research department there is the danger of cut-back in research expenditure either when the production department is not doing well commercially or when it needs to spend money to install new capital facilities.

This applies as much to military spending as to a small private firm. The source of the budget, therefore, needs to be at a sufficiently high level where the special nature of R & D budgets hitherto described, particularly its stability, will be borne in mind and where conflicts with other budget holders can expect to be resolved in the light of sound judgement of the overall objectives of the whole organisation.

EXPENDITURE CONTROL

A budget is of course only of value if there is some control of expenditure as related to the budget and it becomes a matter of skilful judgement in an R & D department to decide the degree and type of financial control required. Basically there will be two types of control. One in which authorisation of expenditure is limited at certain amounts for certain staff levels or responsibilities. Clearly an assistant scientist will not be able to authorise as high an expenditure as a more senior man; this helps the budget holder to exercise some control over the heavier types of expenditure. The other is by returning the actual costs as they arise against different elements in the budget. It is here that over-complexity needs to be avoided since if everything were costed meticulously not only would an army of accountants be necessary, but the scientists and their assistants would be spending a large part of their time compiling records. Certainly the present tendency is towards stricter and more detailed cost accounting but the scientist will have grave doubts as to whether the returns in terms of efficiency in scientific creativity justify it.

Expenditure reporting procedures should be formed and regular returns made, perhaps once a month, so that the project manager and the research director know how their budget is proceeding. A project which is not proceeding in line with budget forecasts needs attention although, as has been previously stated, it does not follow that there must be anything wrong with it technically. However, re-budgeting and re-allocation of resources may well be desirable.

The function of financial control in the laboratory is not therefore to control the scientific programme but to set up boundaries within which research operations can be carried out and to maintain them in accordance with the general authorisation of the parent body.

CRITICAL PATH NETWORKS FOR CONTROL OF RESEARCH PROJECTS

As we have seen in Chapter 4 critical path plans and branched networks can be used for creating a research strategy plan, and the degree of detail in it will depend on the type of project, its uncertainty and whether the benefit/cost ratio is high or not.

The research manager will have played a significant part in setting up the strategy plan and it will be used in many discussions relative to preliminary preparation for the laboratory to take on the work.

When the decision has been made, however, to accept the project, the actual research work must begin, and it is highly likely that for the actual scheduling of work a much more detailed version of the strategy/plan, which might be called the working plan, will have to be drawn up. This will indicate the responsibilities that fall on different sections so that staff, resources, materials can be planned to be brought together at the right time by those responsible. In this way the network can form a useful tool for starting the execution of a project.

Even this working plan, which represents the overall plan, may well not be in sufficient detail for every worker on the project, and he will be encouraged to write his own detailed working plan or study plan, delineating his tasks and the resources he has to seek more surely. This will enable his supervisor to vet his proposals to ensure that they are adequate in themselves and that they fit satisfactorily into the overall working plan and strategy.

The next element in execution and control of a project will be to keep up-to-date the networks so produced. Variation will occur because resources do not become available when planned for, because tasks fail to be carried out in the time allowed, or when new options arise. All the various types of networks have to be updated at varying intervals depending on the extent of departures from control points that occur. A project will not be controlled merely by updating the networks, of course, unless they are used by the managers to detect the trends, estimate the influence on the project objective and take remedial action such as allocating extra resources, buying effort outside the organisation, or developing alternative methods of contributing to the end in view.

If necessary, documentation to progress the different elements in a network can be arranged so that the project leader is aware of trends away from the plan before the modified network appears.

The particular skill of conducting R & D within the constraints of time, money, resource requirements and towards meaningful end-points will not be acquired simply by using network techniques. An able project leader will meet the end requirement without formal network help; a poorer performer will not meet it with the best techniques available. But in general, and particularly with more complex projects lasting several years, network assistance should improve the performance of both the good and the less good.

Thus we can use critical path networks, or, perhaps some simpler technique for simpler projects such as flow-line charts, to establish a control over the pursuit of an R & D programme. The detailed use of such techniques will be in the hands of the research manager, but they are also invaluable to the director in monitoring how the various projects that he is concerned with are shaping up to the research plan upon which the project selection was made, and to enable him to take corrective action in the right direction if the objectives of the research are not being realised.

Where we have satisfactory budget and cost control arrangements and suitable programme control arrangements of the network type, we have a measure of control over how a project is coming along both in general terms and specifically in relation to resources and other inputs, but they only indirectly give control information about how individual members of the research team are performing relative to their tasks in the project as a whole.

At this point we are concerned with the style of management as between different staff levels.

MANAGEMENT BY EXCEPTION

One such style, known as management by exception, is an arrangement whereby only exceptional events are referred to a higher level of management, others being dealt with according to the general principles laid down in the project programme with whatever flexibility is appropriate to the particular level. It becomes the duty of a given researcher or manager to refer such exceptional events to the next superior officer, but the superior will himself become aware of exceptional happenings by the feedback information from cost control, network or other techniques of communication. With the knowledge that an exceptional happening is occurring, the superior officer will probe deeply into the activities surrounding that exception and particularly into the activities of the staff directly or indirectly concerned and will hopefully find some way of alleviating the effects of the 'exception' and get the project as nearly back to programme as possible. In 'management by exception' lower levels of authority are encouraged to take full responsibility for day-to-day decisions and only to obtain approval for decisions that are precedent-setting or cause deviation from agreed plans. This management style has the great advantage that it only uses the senior manager's time when his superior experience can most usefully be used. Inevitably a close probing of any situation gives rise not only to examination of what has gone adrift to cause the 'exception' but also to many other departures from ideal practice which can be put right at the same time.

MANAGEMENT BY OBJECTIVES

An opposite style has, however, recently been gaining popularity throughout many technical operations from industrial production to hospital management, known as 'management by objectives'. This is a technique by which targets are fixed as a basis for achieving greater effectiveness throughout the whole of an organisation or part of an organisation.

The system involves the fixing of agreed and realistic targets between a manager and his staff in as precise terms as possible.

In a production operation the terms may well be quantitative, but in a research and development context they will be related to the objective of the work and are not likely to be expressed in quantitative terms. The factors which impede the attainment of these objectives are then identified and courses of action, including training, are agreed in order to remove them. The results achieved are periodically appraised between manager and staff and new targets set where desirable. Targets should be clear and realistic and should contribute effectively to the aims of the organisation. The approach is based on the view that targets agreed by a manager and his subordinates are in themselves an incentive and that they form a yardstick against which performance can be measured. It can also be claimed that it becomes easier for line management to appraise projects in terms of the expected benefits; it is easier to assess the performance of individuals and check that work loads are right: the MBO records provide a concise, well-organised information system about the work of an organisation; improve resource control; provide quicker response to technical problems and to changes in 'market' requirements; facilitate better long-range planning. [55]

The problem of applying MBO or adapting it to the environment and purposes of a research establishment is, however, a challenging one. It is not easy to define objectives in terms which are precise enough to be meaningful when appraisal takes place, for the results of the research will have conditioned the objective. However, the shorter-term components into which it is necessary to break down the tasks are usually capable of reasonably precise definition.

One analysis of the way in which an MBO scheme can be set up to deal with R & D is given as follows: [56]

1. The general objectives of each R & D project are broken down into detailed short-term objectives which can be quantified in terms of the technical results expected and the target dates by which they are to be achieved. For each such objective the staff and other resources allocated are listed and the methods of monitoring progress are defined. The whole of the work of each division is defined in this way. The breakdown usually needs 3 or 4 stages of refinement, starting with project objectives, out of which are defined a

number of tasks. The tasks are further broken down into jobs and at any particular time these can be characterised by specific actions required. In the hierarchy from project objectives down to specific actions the time-scale of the objectives decreases and the degree of precision with which they are defined increases.

2. The organisation of the staff and the allocation of work are arranged so that every individual is made clearly accountable for the achievement of specific objectives.

3. The definition of technical objectives, target dates and methods of monitoring progress should not be regarded as the prerogative of senior management and imposed from above. They should be evolved by discussion at all levels so that each manager feels that he has a part in determining his own objectives in relation to those of the project as a whole and of influencing the definition of objectives at a higher level. Whatever the level at which objectives are being discussed there has to be a continued mingling of two counter-currents; one is the information on larger policy decisions or changes in requirements (what the 'market' needs or might need); the other is the information and ideas about technical developments and new possibilities (what is available or could be made available, and at what cost). All managers should be encouraged to become fully involved in this process of information exchange and it should be the basis for the formulation and review of objectives at the regular progress meetings described below.

4. A system of progress meetings is set up to ensure that the objectives of each project and the progress made are regularly reviewed. The system will vary with circumstances but would be roughly on the lines shown in table 6.1 (p. 201).

There would, of course be more frequent *ad hoc* discussions, but meetings of the type shown in the table should be instituted on a firm time-table. It is important that the progress reviews should deal only with essentials – key results to be achieved. The junior member of the discussion should be encouraged to define his own objectives and should be given as much freedom as possible to achieve them in his own way. For example, the two-monthly job review meetings should be run by the section head, and if the research manager joins in he should avoid taking control of the meeting.

5. A complete but fairly brief account of the objectives, resource allocations and progress of each project is maintained in a project record file. The project record files are the central feature of the MBO system in this R & D application. They are loose-leaf files and they contain the following items:

(a) A list of the project objectives, task objectives and job objectives with the names of section heads responsible for tasks. This is updated at 12-month intervals.

(b) An organisation chart and a record of staff allocation to tasks. This is updated at 6-month intervals.

(c) A record of project expenditure compared with budget. This is updated at 4-week intervals.

(d) For each task a statement of its objectives and a short background note summarising the state of the art, recent advances, current problems and forecasts of future developments. This background note is updated at 6-month intervals.

(e) For each job a statement of its objective and a series of progress sheets stating the situation at each (2-monthly) progress review and listing actions of individual staff.

The provision of maintenance of items (a), (b) and (c) are usually the responsibility of the research manager. The necessary information on expenditure and manpower can be derived from the existing administration information services but it would be desirable to provide a more detailed breakdown. The responsibility for providing the information in items (d) and (e) is mainly that of the section head responsible for each task. He supplies copies of the progress sheets for the group and department files and also circulates copies to all his professional staff. These sheets fulfil the role of conventional minutes of meetings in providing information and in reminding staff of actions placed on them. Complete project record files are maintained by research manager and director but the section heads may prefer to maintain files for their tasks only. It may be useful to keep the department copies of the files on a magnetic tape system with video display for rapid reference and intercomparison at various level discussions. The project record files should be treated as formal documents and it is important that they be kept clear and concise, excluding all non-essential information such as correspondence or supporting documents. They should be regarded as constituting the R & D manager's control and information system. The complete files or just the lists of objectives and the technical notes can be given wide circulation to professional staff as a means of keeping them well informed.

6. The work of each professional staff member is reviewed at 6-month intervals in terms of the specific objectives towards which he has been working. His progress is noted and his objectives for the next 6-month period are reviewed. These reviews should be conducted by the research manager with the appropriate section head(s). The results should be summarised and filed in the research manager's staff review file, a personal copy of each man's review note being sent to him.

The effort to install and operate such a system is by no means insignificant. It has been estimated that for a typical R & D department (say about 40 professional scientists) to install MBO from scratch would need about six man-months of work by a team of management advisers plus about six man-months of work by the staff at research manager/section head level. Thereafter, however, the effort needed to maintain the system is probably not significantly greater than for other methods of divisional management.

It is expected that the improvements obtained should amount to at least 10 per cent of output.

The main points of difference between the implementation of 'standard' MBO and the R & D version described above arise from the smaller role played by the external advisers in the R & D version. In standard MBO the external advisers interview each manager to determine the precise content of his job, to define job improvement objectives and to analyse the organisational structure. As a result, the exercise of introducing MBO automatically brings with it the benefits of an independent audit of the efficiency of utilisation of resources and a critical appraisal of the organisational structure. In the

R & D version, however, the organisational structure is defined by the division director, and the section task and job objectives are defined by the section heads themselves (with advice from the management development advisers). Thus the audit of resources and objectives is not fully independent and, although still a salutary exercise, it may be less thorough. However, the R & D version requires less effort to install and once set up it provides the material for further refinement at various levels of line management and for independent audit later if required.

CASH FLOW DIAGRAMS AS CONTROL TECHNIQUES

The management of an R & D project so that it conforms to the initial plan or is suitably adjusted to the evolution of the project is not in itself sufficient if the project is related to a development which is eventually 'marketable'. Before research passes over to a project phase leading to a development, a cash flow diagram of the type shown in Fig. 1.1 will have been prepared, or at any rate some reasoning will have been gone through which enables a judgement to be made that if the research follows a certain plan, a certain useful practical application will eventually emerge.

Thus, with a military project it may be adjudged that a potential enemy could suffer damage over a certain period before his defences were built up. With a health project it may be judged that a given treatment would take a certain amount of money when applied generally, relieve a certain amount of suffering and result in a certain economic saving.

During the course of the research plan something may happen to alter the eventual expected outcome. The anticipated commercial profit may appear to have diminished because of other happenings in the market; the potential enemy may have built a defence against our development sooner than expected; another treatment may have appeared which will prove cheaper or more effective than ours.

The periodic drawing up of such cash flow diagrams or reviews of the case for conducting the research should, therefore, be discussed as a control to indicate whether any of the reasons for shutting down or modifying the project discussed in Chapter 4 have materialised.

CAUTION IN USE OF CONTROL TECHNIQUES

The effect of the use of any control techniques on the research worker has always to be carefully considered. They can easily see them, and often rightly so, as techniques for monitoring their progress and criticising any failure to meet targets, whether of money, technical success or time. But in research, plans should be regarded as drafts of the way things might go. If they do not go that way, the plan needs to be altered. That plans going the way they are drafted makes life easier for researcher, planner and management, should act as a spur to the researcher to give his best assistance in the preparation of the plan – which he should always be invited to do – and to adhere to it as closely as possible. The goals set up by plans should be regarded as key decision areas rather than key result areas, and one should talk of indicators to action rather than standards to be enforced.

Of course, in inviting researchers to contribute to planning we should note the differences in personal response that can occur. One man will be enthusiastic to promise a maximum contribution at a minimum cost: another will guard against not meeting goals, by pessimistic forecasting. Planners and managers must learn to interpret the personal response.

COMMUNICATIONS

However large or however small a research department is, its function is to convert the thoughts in the scientists' minds into a body of information in the mind of the director who can then contribute to the policy of his parent organisation. One objective within a research establishment, therefore, is to ensure that the thinking of the scientist is directed towards likely fruition in respect of the needs of the parent organisation, with a minimum of effort and of waste: another is to ensure that the director receives a proper distillation of what is in the scientist's mind: another is that the director should have a similar dialogue with his parent organisation: another is that, having established a research task, the scientist should pursue it with the greatest efficiency. Achieving these objectives is largely dependent on communications, and there are few more important tasks for a director than to ensure that the best and most fitting communication network is available to his department.

COMMUNICATIONS GENERALLY

Communications are vital to any form of social life. The nature of information and ideas, the means of transmission, the direction of the transmission and the perception of the recipient, all are part of the communication process.

They are particularly important in organisations and organisational segments like research departments that must deal with uncertainty, are complex, and have a technology that does not permit easy routinisation.

The process of communication is relational: one party is the sender and one is the receiver and personal relationships come into what is sent and what is received, leading to disortion. The sender supplies information to a receiver having in mind what he thinks of the receiver, his ability, his knowledge of the subject, whether he likes him or not, what his power in the organisation is. The receiver of information receives it 'with a grain of salt' relative to his relationship with the sender, putting him into a category, which when he stereotypes it as good or bad leads to some distortion of the information.

This is not necessarily a disruptive procedure, for communications should provide accurate information only at the density needed, and coloured with the appropriate emotional overtones in relation to all members who need the communications content. [57]

DOWNWARD COMMUNICATION

Katz and Kahn [28] have identified five elements of downwards communication.

(a) Job instruction – where by one means or another, a subordinate is told what to do. This is fairly straightforward although many techniques such as training, job descriptions, have to be used.

(b) Rationale – the more subtle exercise of putting over the concept of the organisation which one wants the subordinates to appreciate. The extent to which this is carried out depends on the philosophy of the communicator in relation to his subordinates and also the genuine necessity of avoiding confusion, indeed chaos, in giving out more of the higher rationale than the subordinates can, or want to, absorb.

(c) Information – regarding future procedures, practices, tasks of the organisation. This too is relatively straightforward as for (a).

(d) Feedback – from the subordinate regarding his performance. This is always difficult and we have seen how it forms a continuous part of management by objectives. Despite problems, however, it has a necessary function in the vertical communication process.

(e) Ideology – the attempt of the organisation to indoctrinate subordinates with emotional understanding and acceptance of the goals of the organisation (or sub-department).

All these elements are involved in a research organisation, but they become more complex with the upper echelons of the organisation, or indeed wherever the subordinate is an expert himself.

Categorisation to take some account of this problem is given by Parsons [58] who considers different levels, at each of which these elements have different force

Institutional – concerned with relating the organisation to the external world. Directing level.

Managerial – concerned with internal administration of the organisation, or carrying out of the decisions made at director level.

Technical – involved with the translation of information passed by management into specific tasks and their direction.

DISRUPTIVE EFFECTS OF HIERARCHY ON COMMUNICATIONS

The complex nature of vertical communications is further

compounded by the disruptive effects that a hierarchy can itself have on communications.

(a) There is a common tendency for people to react more easily with those at their own level than with members higher in the organisation.

(b) There is equally a tendency for those in lower status to look up to those in high status and frequently to distort communications so that they put themselves in a good light.

(c) As we have seen, part of the communication function is feedback or error-correction. This is likely to be reasonably successful on a horizontal basis and vertically downwards but it is much less likely to act vertically upwards, though it is just as necessary.

Finally, the fact that different levels of an organisation are likely to work at different levels of thought and ability produces a resultant real intellectual barrier which causes communications difficulties.

This is particularly true in a research department. There, more than in most organisations, the higher levels are likely to be chosen for high intellectual ability; at the same time, the intellectual ability of the subordinate is not only high but he is more expert in the research work that is going on. Hence the higher echelons become able generalists with a lack of understanding of the research work – which surprises, confuses and annoys the younger subordinate.

In such situations it needs to be better understood that the function of the hierarchy is largely one of co-ordination.

UPWARDS COMMUNICATIONS

More than in most other types of organisation, it is necessary in a research organisation for communications to pass upwards as well as downwards – indeed it is the information at the base of the structure which entirely sustains the organisation. But it is here that information passing can be most affected by hierarchical considerations and by socio-emotive factors, even in a laboratory. The person communicating upward can more easily see threats to himself, his work or his work group which he would wish to ward off. Equally he always has the task of filtering and editing for condensation purposes to give a communication acceptable up the line. However impartially and efficiently he may seek to do this it is not an easy task.

COMMUNICATIONS AND 'CLIENTS'

All organisations react with some element of their environment which may be regarded as 'clients' and this may take place at different levels in the hierarchy. An industrial research department which has technical services as part of its activities will operate 'client' relationships at quite low levels. A Ministry of Defence laboratory may well only inter-relate outside at the higher levels. But much the same communications problems will occur as internally and they will be dependent on whether they and the client himself regards the communication as being downward, upward or horizontal, taking into consideration the relative power of the two sides. It is generally desirable to minimise the hierarchical tendencies in such relationships.

HORIZONTAL COMMUNICATIONS

Horizontal communications have received less attention than vertical ones. For one thing they are less obviously a force in hierarchical organisations. In fact, however, there are more horizontal communications than vertical, both because there are more prople to interact horizontally and because people find it easier to interrelate at their own level.

Within an organisational sub-unit particularly, this type of communication is critical for effective system functioning, although in research establishments it needs to be positively fostered unless horizontal co-ordination is necessary to carry out the tasks of the sub-unit. Horizontal communication is vital where co-ordination is necessary, for supervisors cannot conceive of every eventuality and plan for it. Indeed, if there are not communications necessities for getting the work done the natural tendency for association of people at the same level will take forms which are irrelevant or destructive of proper organisational functioning. [59, 28]

It is, therefore, beneficial to allow work groups at every level of a hierarchy to have some task-orientated communications left to them. This is particularly true in research departments where association for cross-fertilisation purposes is desirable and it will be made much easier if association is necessary for direct task reasons.

Such associations should not, however, be fostered to a point where horizontal levels produce a collective entity of interpretation of goals which may be a collective distortion. This can apply vertically in sub-units as well as horizontally.

Communication horizontally between sub-units does not in fact occur to such a great extent although obedience to the theory that all such communications should proceed upwards to the point of common control would totally clog the communications system. A sufficiently co-operative attitude for inter sub-unit communication to occur is, therefore, necessary.

In a research department, however, where common tasks between sub-units are not likely to be very numerous, it is even more necessary positively to foster some interaction because productive work often nowadays arises from the association of disciplines which are not normally closely related.

One clearly needs to face the basic difficulties of communications in complex, hierarchical systems. The facts of organisational life preclude the development of a perfect communications system. Also it has to be remembered that, with communications as with the rest of organisational properties, the system is continually changing and the communications network correct for one set of circumstances is not right for another, and improvement in one communications relationship may lead to deterioration in another.

Downs [60] suggests some devices for reducing distortions in communications. For example, the duplication of reports, which spreads information further than it might otherwise go, the suggestion that communications recipients should appreciate the biases of information senders and, in vertical communications, the superior should occasionally bypass intermediate subordinates, though this should be done openly and carefully so as not to affect the morale of those bypassed.

COMMUNICATIONS IN THE LABORATORY

In a very small laboratory the task is relatively simple. The director can keep in personal touch with all his staff and talk between them is all that is necessary. The director can then guide each worker both towards the overall laboratory objective and towards achieving it most efficiently. At the same time he receives his knowledge of what thoughts the scientific work is throwing up and frames the conclusions into recommendations for further action upon them.

In a very large laboratory communication is, as we have seen, necessarily much more complex because of the necessity to subdivide functions into specialist groups with a hierarchy of management. In a typical large laboratory there will be a split between research activities, service activities (particularly engineering), and administration. Each of these departments will be further subdivided, the research department into different scientific divisions dependent on discipline or projects, the others into specialist activities like photography, analysis, library, accounts, personnel, etc. In such an organisation problems of communication occur:

(a) between the 'working' staff and managing or directing staff at all levels of the hierarchy, both upwards and downwards,

(b) between the specialist group and scientific users and managers,

(c) within individual teams of workers,

(d) between separate groups.

One of the purposes of communication will be to digest and classify all the information that comes into the organisation, whether it comes through individuals or correspondence from the many contacts the laboratory has with external organisations, through published literature, or from other parts of the parent organisation. This information has to be disseminated to the right people as quickly and as usefully as possible. Another purpose of communication will be to assist in the development of ideas about and solutions to the organisation's problems. For example, the majority of technological problems will require the conjoint thought of a number of research workers together with engineers, analysts, etc., and frequently parts of the research programmes of one team will need to be undertaken by another team either inside or outside the organisation.

There is no ideal method of dealing with all these communication problems, no single solution to its organisation, but the following ideas are relevant to sound practice in this field.

1. Of first importance is the necessity of fostering the concept of the desirability of thorough communications, so that workers recognise the value to themselves and to the work of the establishment of open-mindedness in the reception of ideas and help from other sources and of themselves contributing to the communicating processes.

2. In all organisations one particular barrier to communication exists in the requirements of 'security' of the work of an organisation. Paradoxically it is frequently the establishments with the greatest needs of security such as military research establishments where the greatest effort is made to ensure open communication and publishing wherever possible. This is done by putting a good deal of effort into formalising the subjects and levels of control so that the research workers know what is open and can be encouraged accordingly. Such methods might well be adopted where commercial security only is of concern.

3. Other barriers to communication also exist, notably the problems of language. It is impossible to communicate all that has happened during a research project so it is important in communicating the essence of such work both to consider what a likely reader wishes to know and to write it in a manner which is likely to be easily understood. Both these things are difficult to accomplish, and are themselves two-way mechanisms in that the nature of what the reader wishes to know must first be communicated to the writer and a written report should only be used for the purpose for which it was intended.

4. The personality of the communicator is important. Some research workers wish to hide their work until they are quite sure that it is satisfactory and complete: others wish to burst into print almost before they have done any experimentation. Both have to be guided in the direction of communicating at different levels of thoroughness depending on the relationship of their work to that of the rest of the organisation. Sometimes periodic statements or laboratory

reports (perhaps quarterly) are called for on all work. This can be useful but must not be considered as a substitute for full writing of reports when a task is complete.

5. A distinction needs to be drawn between reports of research work carried out and reports required by management for some other purposes – the justification of a given research programme or of the purchase of a large piece of equipment or reporting the completed work to a higher authority. The latter are likely to fall to the manager or even the director but only after adequate discussion with the researchers concerned. There is a lot to be said for having official writers for this type of management paper, since research workers generally resent doing such work and managers can be too busy.

6. Official writers might be housed in the technical information department which is also the point of entry of the largest flow of information in the form of publications. Facilitating the flow of information to those who need it is a primary function of such a department. It may be done by the general methods of circulating indices and abstracts relevant to the work of the station, or in a way more personal to the needs of an individual worker by searching literature relevant to the known work of that particular worker. The latter is particularly useful when a man is starting to work in a new field. Indeed, in a technological research department, particularly where the work frequently swings from one subject to another, inefficiency can easily arise from workers doing research or developing techniques which are already known elsewhere, and a great contribution can be made to the productivity of a research worker by an information officer actively concerning himself to provide such a service.

In some laboratories the patent officer who is in touch with a lot of what is going on both inside and outside a laboratory can help in this respect, but a strong case could be made for specially suited and trained officers to develop such a service in a positive fashion.

7. The needs of new employees require special concern and a firm attempt should be made to integrate them into their new community with a minimum of difficulty if for no other reason than that they will be the more efficient for 'knowing

the ropes'. Induction courses, special lectures related to the R & D department, the availability of suitable booklets describing the organisation, services available, safety rules, etc., are all methods which can be useful in this respect.

8. In many stations, particularly those remote from large towns, it is particularly difficult to ensure that research workers are kept in touch with what is happening in their field in a general sense. A generous encouragement to attending learned society or professional meetings is very desirable (and the tendency of administrators to cut the travelling costs for such purposes sometimes needs to be fought strongly) and it is a help to conduct colloquia at the station with visiting authorities participating.

9. The corresponding problem of keeping different groups of workers in touch with each other in the same station is also a particularly difficult one, and sometimes internal colloquia as well as wide circulation of research reports can help, in addition to the director and his managers showing continual alertness in arranging appropriate meetings.

10. In some organisations correspondence can only be signed at some senior level which has the merit that the senior man has the opportunity of knowing in detail what is going on around him. However, this can have a stultifying effect on less senior staff, tends to diminish self confidence, and slows the rate of progress of the work. But it is probably no bad thing that copies of all correspondence in a division, both incoming and outgoing, should find their way into the hands of the divisional director at some time not too far prolonged from its initiation.

11. Where the techniques described earlier of critical path networking or management by objectives are employed, they will continually throw up documentation in the form of revised network statements or analytical reports, which provide a means of communication between the scientists, engineers and directing staff which is of great value in controlling the activities of a department.

12. In the conduct of research work related to projects whether the project be oriented towards a technological end-point or whether it be purely an interdisciplinary scientific enquiry there will certainly be the necessity of a formal

committee structure – committees for cross-fertilisation of ideas between different contributing parties, for discussion to arrive at suitable programmes of work, for communication between different levels of the hierarchy to effect the interplay of growing scientific knowledge and 'market' forces, at different directing levels of the hierarchy so that the activities of different divisions can be dovetailed together. Such formal committees are of considerable value in the communication network and should be established consciously and with considerable care. Equally, however, their disbandment at appropriate stages of a project needs to be considered with equal consciousness and care. Committees have a strong life force and will persist long after their usefulness has ended unless dealt with firmly.

It will thus be seen that communications of many sorts provide essential tools in the control of R & D activities in relation to its objectives as well as assisting in the provision of a good environment in which research can be carried out.

DIFFERENCE BETWEEN MANAGEMENT AND DIRECTION

In the control of research projects the functions of the management and directing levels must be disentangled as far as possible although this is by no means easy to accomplish. Clearly it is for the director to decide, in consultation with his research managers and in relation to the methods and requirements of the parent organisation, on the techniques to be used, the style of management, the general framework of the control mechanisms and communications network. Equally clearly the main burden of operating all these techniques will fall on the research managers and it is important to be sure that research managers are not loaded without adequate technical assistance, in order that they can exercise a strong influence on the research itself. What is less clear is the extent of involvement at directing level when 'danger signals' may be thrown up by the operation of the control system. The research manager may sometimes take action independently; sometimes the research manager will call in the director for advice or because correcting actions are beyond his level of control; sometimes the director will find it necessary to involve himself deeply in the situation signalled as 'dangerous'. The degree of involvement of the director will depend greatly on the characteristics of both manager and director but it is desirable that relationships between them should be built up so that the line of demarcation will be tacitly understood between them, even though neither thinks it optimum, so that the research manager should not be frustrated by what he considers as either over or under involvement by his director. (See also Chapter 11.)

THE END-POINT OF PROJECT-ORIENTATED RESEARCH

Having carefully selected a project and controlled the research and development activity essential to it, it is important that the end-point of the R & D activity should be stated in some definite terms which relate to the project, whether it be a new process or a new product, and whether it be in chemical or engineering fields, or in agriculture or health. The natural end-point of a research activity is a research report and it is important that such a report should be written to a scientific standard consistent with the quality of the research itself. It cannot be better but it is not at all unusual to find reports not adequately presenting the sound scientific work that has been carried out and it is a sound idea that all scientific reports should be seen at the directing level with the aim of insisting on high standards of reporting. The research report itself is not, however, very often a suitable end-point to a project-orientated research and development. A document is needed which places the work in the context of the project objective. Thus if the objective is to build a pilot plant or a full-scale plant it is important that a specification should be written and an operating schedule drawn up, representing the extent to which the research has fixed the parameters and conditions for such a plant to operate. The attempt to do this to the satisfaction of the engineer who is to build the plant will often indicate areas where the research has been inadequate for the project concerned so that more research will need to be done. If the project end-point is a prototype mechanism or a commercial engineering unit then similarly the right end-point of the research is a specification containing the information relative to the design that the research has given rise to. If the research leads to a new process, whether it be in a chemical plant or a new scheme for growing crops, a process manual should be produced stating clearly what the new process is to the extent that the research has defined it. Again this exercise might reveal after discussion with the factory manager or the practising farmer that the research is incomplete so a feedback to further research is called for.

If the research and development activity in all these cases is terminated solely at the research report stage, there is a danger that it will not be sufficiently understood by the engineer/chemist/farmer or, because the research deficiencies have not emerged, that it will simply not be accepted by them as serving their practical ends. Many sound pieces of project-orientated research fail to end up as 'hardware' for these reasons.

The long-term research worker should be encouraged to carry a responsibility for exploring with others the means by which the translation of his work into processes of material application may be done most effectively. He should be encouraged to consider himself a member of a team extending over development, design and application, whose efforts he must guide, to whose needs he must respond, and whose difficulties will stimulate and guide him. It follows that the production of the documents aligning the research with the project objectives is even more important than the research reports and while the latter can only be effectively produced by the scientists, the specification type document which has to have an eye to the market, to 'commercial' security as well as to the end product may to advantage be written by collaboration between the scientist and a specialist in specification writing. This is perhaps even more true where the end-point or one of the products of the research is a patent which needs to be filed as a commercially viable property.

PATENTS AND POSITIVE PUBLICATION POLICY

Creative ideas are assets to an organisation just as much as buildings, machinery, etc., and it is important that the organisation protects and uses these assets in the interests of the organisation.

Three aspects of this are important:

(a) Legal rights acquired by the issue of patents.
(b) The trade secret type of protection.
(c) Control by a positive publication policy.

PATENTS AND COPYRIGHTS

Patents and copyrights are legal rights granted by governments to the inventor or the owner of an invention. One important question to ask at the completion of a research project is whether or not a patent could be obtained, and if so, whether it should. Many sound research results do not yield a patentable idea and in any case, the fact that large sums of money have been expended in the research and development efforts does not in itself provide the justification for filing a patent, or in some cases a series of patents. Patents, including as they do, searches and possibly litigation, may not always be warranted.

The first step in considering a patent is to obtain the views of the patent expert as to whether a patent is likely to be accepted by the Patent Office or challenged by someone else. This initial search is relatively inexpensive, but important.

A second step is to assess the market potential of the invention. Researchers are inclined to press for the patenting of their work but this is only justified if the idea appears to have some potential for marketing although not necessarily by the organisation in which the discovery has been made. Indeed, much patent protection is obtained to avoid the possibility that someone else who can market the knowledge does not in due course discover the same thing or learn of it in some other way and duly patent it with the exclusion of benefit to the original inventor.

If these two steps have been carried out satisfactorily and the idea is still considered worthy of patenting, the patent expert will make a more thorough search. This will indicate what parts of the new discovery are patentable and what parts, if any, have already been anticipated. (The search may even reveal other inventions which are better than the one proposed, in which case it may pay the organisation to drop its own patenting ideas and license the better one, or abandon the project.) The extent of coverage to be aimed at will then be determined and the patent expert proceeds to draw up the specification. It is as well to go for as wide a coverage as is possible from the information available and not to be too modest with claims.

When the patent has been secured, its economic potential must be realised by

(a) Manufacture and selling of the product implied.

(b) Licensing other manufacturers to make the product and obtaining royalties in some form.

(c) Both manufacture and licensing of the product.

(d) Using the patent to protect a current product until the time is ripe, economically, for its exploitation. Protective patenting is important for the future security of the company's market.

One important aspect of patents where they arise from research work in an R & D organisation is the ownership of the patent. An organisation would be most unwise not to have a clear understanding of the rights of the organisation *vis-à-vis* the researcher on the one hand and the sponsor of the research on the other.

So far as the researcher is concerned it is usual and sensible that he should assign his rights to the organisation. This does not mean that the researcher should not receive some extra reward from a fruitful patent, although this should be seen in the context of the reservation that whether a researcher is put on to work which will yield a fruitful patent or not is as much a matter of luck as of creative skill, so the direct reward for an invention should be kept small so as to stimulate, yet not alienate the colleagues of the researcher.

Where a patent arises from research work sponsored by an outside organisation (such as the government) or from research that the organisation itself sponsors outside, again it is necessary to be clear as to who owns the patent rights. In general it will be true that the organisation which pays for the research owns the patent rights but it is usually acceptable for the researching organisation to retain some rights. For example, the government might agree to the organisation doing the research having civilian as against military rights, or to some commercial rights for initial manufacture where the product is widely applicable.

What is important is that a clear understanding should be established and that it should be sufficiently fair between both organisations for the maximum stimulus to be given to successful research.

TRADE SECRET PROTECTION

The disadvantage of patent protection is that it is a form of publication of the results of the research. It is, therefore, an invitation to a competitor or other potential user to make use of it, either secretly or by finding a way around the patent.

The alternative that may be practised is the trade secret type of protection which is obtained simply by restricting the knowledge to those staff who are assumed to be loyal and proceed to manufacture the new product without revealing how it is made. By this means the market can be entered earlier and well ahead of competitors who can continue to be denied the market. This method has the disadvantage that it leads to the necessary exercising of commercial secrecy controls and can also lead to industrial espionage. Equally, processes can be licensed on the basis of 'know-how' without patents necessarily being taken out.

POSITIVE PUBLICATION POLICY

Allied to the control exercised by patent protection or trade secret protection is the policy to be used for the publication of research work.

As has been stated elsewhere in this book, it is most desirable that research workers should be allowed freedom to publish some of their work. This is in the best interests of the image of the research department as well as being a necessary stimulus to the researcher, who if he is a good researcher will feel a need to establish himself in his profession as well as with his employers.

This does not, however, mean that a man should have the freedom to publish what he likes independently of what is in the interests of the research department and its parent authority. It is necessary, therefore, to set up a mechanism by which a positive publications policy can be activated and maintained. This means both vetting publication proposals to ensure that they do not give too much away (this may mean nothing more than modifying a paper to eliminate undesirable things from it), and actively encouraging research staff to write papers and articles in selected media on subjects which it is felt would help the legitimate ends of the parent organisation by being made public.

UTILISING RESEARCH RESULTS

Of course the true end-point of research conducted for practical reasons is not solely any form of documentation, but practical application. Successful research management will, therefore, ask of any research which has reached the documentation end-point 'What do I now do to make this work practically effective?'

Where the work is fully relevant to the work of the parent authority it is likely that avenues will exist in the form of board meetings, technical policy committees, etc., where the research results can be introduced and decisions taken about using them. It should be borne in mind that the obvious exploitation is not necessarily the best. It may pay an organisation not to use an discovery directly, even though relevant to its operations, because a greater return might be obtained from trading it elsewhere. It may not necessarily be considered only for use towards the ends for which it was first sponsored.

Where work is not relevant to the work of the parent authority or only marginally so, the best method of exploitation should be considered carefully. Perhaps it should be protected for direct use in the future, perhaps it should be sold on a know-how licensing basis, perhaps it should be jointly developed with another organisation (maybe making use of the NRDC as a suitable broker). It may even deserve forming the basis of a new diversification enterprise within the organisation, with new production facilities set up to exploit it.

Perhaps, on the other hand, the greatest value to the organisation concerned would arise from making the information freely and widely available either for prestige purposes or because work may come back to the organisation from interested sponsors. This latter type of decision is more likely to be made in organisations like government laboratories or research associations who depend in some way for part of their funds on satisfying the demands of the sponsors in a general fashion. The mechanism for disseminating information of this sort so that it gets into the hands of the people most likely to find it of value is itself a skilled operation. It should not be considered sufficient to have a list of organisations who might be interested and a panel of lecturers to offer to anyone who enquired for a lecture to be given.

A research result may indicate a new field of useful further research which may be of interest to others, such as a government department. In such a case it may be appropriate to submit a proposal to the appropriate department for a sponsored research project – making sure that commercially useful rights are covered in the contract.

The uses of research results should never be considered on too narrow a front and the appointment of an exploitation officer with keen understanding of research usefulness and wide knowledge and contacts is always worth serious consideration – even if only on a part-time basis in a smaller research organisation.

The control of R & D projects will thus be seen itself to involve a spectrum of activities. The development and use of various techniques for direct control of the operation of the project will be followed by decisions about the right way to express the results to protect them, and finally to exploit them. Throughout these activities sound methods of communication provide a lubrication of great importance to successful achievement.

SUMMARY

Having established a research programme, the next step is to control the research and of first consideration here are the maintaining of a high standard of scientific work and the establishing of a high level of research management representation in the hierarchy of the parent authority.

The primary means of control will usually be financial, with the budget coming first. The desirability of special considerations in the budgeting of research are emphasised – changes should only be gradual because of the long-term nature of research and the importance of personnel-orientated costs being uppermost. A five year budget as well as an annual one is desirable.

Types of budgeting and the steps that would be taken in producing a budget are discussed and emphasis placed on delegating responsibility for working to budgets at appropriate working levels.

Budgets must be regarded as of limited usefulness in controlling research other than in ensuring that resources are used on the right projects and to be more useful towards the development end of the research spectrum. Financial control arises from budgeting and overcomplexity needs to be avoided.

Critical path networking is a useful control of research projects only so long as the initial network is updated in the light of experience on the project. It will be operated at different levels with appropriate detail and will enable all levels to take corrective action if the objectives of the research are not being realised.

The style of management plays an important part in controlling R & D with two basic styles, management by exception and management by objectives. The latter is a recent technique which has generally been used for the more formal type of technological operations, but attempts have recently been made to modify this to make it suitable for research type operations and such an attempt is described.

Such control techniques should not be regarded as techniques for monitoring technical success and goals set by plans should be regarded as key decision areas rather than key result areas.

Throughout research management operations, communications act as a binding agent and a lubricator and deserve close attention.

Different processes of communication are examined and categorised and the forces that enter into them identified. A number of ideas relevant to sound practice in communications in the laboratory are mentioned, particularly the need to foster awareness of communication needs, upwards as well as downwards, adjustment to personalities concerned, the types of research report, the special needs of new employees and the problems of keeping research workers in touch with outside activities.

The correct end-point of research work in terms of communication to the next stage is discussed with particular reference to mounting a positive publication policy through patents, trade secret protection and prestige publication.

Since the final end-point of research should be its exploitation for greatest usefulness, steps that should be taken after research is ended for ensuring that its maximum usefulness is considered, as the final control to be exercised.

TABLE 6.1

Topics	Interval between reviews	Staff involved
Review the Projects and objectives their progress and the allocation of resources to them	1 year	Parent organisation, authority and director
Review the Task objectives and their progress, and the allocation of resources to tasks	6 months	Director, research manager, section heads
Review the Job objectives and their progress. Define and review current actions	2 months	Section head with all professional staff (Research manager attends occasionally)

7 Efficiency and productivity in R & D

THE PLACE OF EFFICIENCY IN R & D

Efficiency and productivity in research and development must not be confused as being the same as efficiency in production or ordinary service activities. The greatest output and its highest quality in scientific terms comes from the time and energy of the scientifically productive research workers, and the organiser of a laboratory who has efficiency in mind would have constantly under review ways in which this time and energy can be conserved and the research quality enhanced.

We have already seen that it is a major preoccupation of a scientific director to try to ensure that projects are worked on which give high potential return (not necessarily financial) and which are suitable to the skills of the research workers available. The research worker does not then waste his time on unsuitable low-gain projects.

We have also seen in Chapter 6 how 'control' of research projects can be exercised by a continuous review of the factors which have led to a project being selected and then planned, with attention being paid in due course to the most useful termination of the project. Efficiency in the conduct of research is derived from such control but, perhaps even more importantly, by adjusting the control techniques to the group being controlled. For the degree and type of control will depend on the nature of the resources being used, particularly the use of expensive, large-scale equipment, the type of research – from exploratory to development – and thirdly the nature of the scientists who are being dealt with, bearing in mind that a minimum of direction is to be aimed at. In the conduct of basic or fundamental research a minimum of administrative control is desirable.

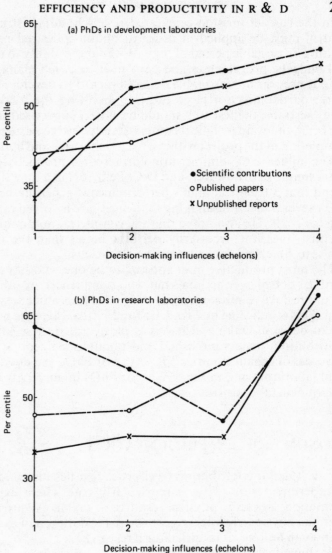

FIG. 7.1 (a) and (b) Performance of researchers as a function of decision-making influences [61]

In the case of mission-orientated research, administrative control must be applied in order to obtain a desired result within a reasonable period of time. Without the ability to control budgets, programmes and personnel, research managers cannot prevent unreasonable delay in regard to development work; particularly for large projects involving the work of many sections, the research should be closely supervised from financial, time and technical content standpoints to ensure the completion of the project within a reasonable time and budget.

The influence of administration on research productivity is not a simple one, however, and D.C. Peltz [61] in a long study found that a technical man's performance is generally better when several 'decision-making influences' are involved in setting his goals. He also noted that the completely autonomous scientist does not necessarily perform better than the man whose technical goals are determined by others.

The most productive man appears to be one who has substantial control over his goals but who is influenced by others. An unproductive situation occurs when the boss alone sets the goal. This is indicated by Figs 7.1(a) and 7.1(b) where the number of decision-making echelons is plotted against scientific contribution, papers published and unpublished reports for two types of organisation: in Fig 7.1(a) for PhDs in a development laboratory and in Fig. 7.1(b) for PhDs in university and government laboratories.

ECONOMY OF EXPERIMENTATION

The next major contribution to effort-saving lies in economy in experimentation. This is particularly true where experimentation uses large physical resources – say an expensively operated physico-chemical rig, or where the duration of experiments can be long, as in agricultural research.

We have seen how careful planning of a research project is desirable, perhaps making use of network planning, in order to organise the general process of the research and how this points up where and what resources of various kinds need to be available. This presupposes that thought is given to the nature of the experimentation and should avoid time-wasting waiting for resources to appear. If carried out sufficiently thoroughly it would also highlight any 'resources' which were not available without further experimentation; for example, a satisfactory chemical analytical technique may not be available and may have to be worked out and its suitability and accuracy studied before the main experimentation can proceed.

Even with sound broad planning, however, many faults can find their way into the actual experimentation; these include

(a) Skilled researchers have to carry out subsidiary aspects of the programme which could be done by less skilled staff.

(b) Experiments are done which are not in direct line to the project requirement or they are done without a definite purpose which gives a definite conclusion.

(c) Insufficient care is taken to characterise starting materials or to study variables which affect the outcome so that results become inconclusive or cannot be interpreted. In complicated work this fault is more easy to recognise by hindsight than foresight but is one that the good experimenter is continually on his guard against.

(d) Too many experiments are done – sometimes simply to occupy time, sometimes out of confusion about what is the objective of the experiment series.

(e) Experiments are done when theory is adequate for the purpose or where they have already been done by someone else.

(f) Experiments are limited to conditions easily accessible in the laboratory so that they do not relate to the practical outcome of the project or they miss an advantage which a larger ranging study may bring to light.

(g) Emphasis may be put towards the experiments which are working out successfuily scientifically rather than covering the broad front necessary to achieve the goal.

(h) The chase for full and complete understanding of a situation or the fear of falling into the trap under (c) sometimes leads to complicated series of experiments being carried out where guide line experiments are all that is necessary at a particular stage of exploration.

Most of these faults are those of lack of experience and can be mitigated by appointing research section leaders or research managers of experience in situations where such errors are likely to arise.

Reference should also be made to the use of statistical methods in experimental design which are of considerable value in economic experimentation, particularly where there are many uncontrolled variables and the duration of experimentation is long. [62]

SCALE OF EXPERIMENTATION

The scale at which experimentation is conducted has considerable importance as related to a technological objective, and if the objective is to be reached with a minimum of effort and time, much care has to be spent on deciding the right scale for different steps of an investigation. The first exploratory work will almost certainly be done on a small scale – even a micro scale if materials are costly. In this way it is more likely that a large number of experiments will be carried out cheaply and quickly. When the exploratory work has pointed the way to a research project, however, the scale of each step needs to be considered. Sometimes optimising experimentation can continue to be carried out at small scale, sometimes certain important sections of (say) a prototype or plant will have to be checked at full scale. Often an intermediate scale will be chosen for prototype or pilot plant between the exploratory laboratory scale and the eventual commercial unit; but this is unnecessary if sufficient scale-up knowledge exists and the tendency is more and more to scale laboratory work and design it so that, related to up-scaling knowledge, it will produce enough information for full-scale design. If a pilot scale is envisaged its size needs to be related carefully to the eventual commercial unit so that scale-up is seen to be admissible. Thus if the objective is a chemical plant of a very novel kind to operate at 3000 ton/day, a pilot plant running at even 1 ton per day – which could be large by laboratory standards – may not be sufficiently convincing for the potential 'customer'.

Similar principles apply to the size of experiments in agricultural, medical or other fields.

TOOLS OF RESEARCH

Another major contributor to the saving of the time and energy of research work is that they should have available modern tools as technical aids to efficiency. The use of computers is an example of a research tool, which to be considered exhaustively would require a book in itself. The director's chief concern is to maintain a balance, providing just the computing facility which will encourage the optimum use. Too little computerisation can waste the time of researchers, doing time-consuming calculations; too much encourages staff to use computerisation for the sake of it. There is the danger that much time can be wasted in complicating what should be a simple research pattern by producing voluminous results to be 'handled by the computer'.

Allied to computers for calculation purposes is electronic equipment for the automation, automatic experimental control and experimental data handling peripheral to computers which play an increasing and valuable part in efficiently run laboratories. Using such equipment, more experiments can be conducted over shorter periods, with a considerable saving of experimental assistant staff. There has been a very great increase in the usage of this type of equipment in large laboratories over the last ten years.

New research techniques such as electron probe microscopy, electron paramagnetic resonance, neutron diffraction, radioactivation analysis, infrared spectroscopy, optical rotatory dispersion, mass spectrometry and experimental nuclear reactors can also contribute to greatly increased research productivity because the research worker is enabled economically to obtain more information from his experiments and in some cases take steps which were impossible before.

Although there is no substitute for the high intellectual powers of first rate scientists it is equally true that no likely assembly of brains can accomplish advanced research undertakings without the tools. Care must be taken, therefore, to ensure that the best instrumentation is available relative to the tasks of a research group, and also that the operation and maintenance of such specialised equipment is separate, adequate and convenient to the use of scientists.

ASSISTANCE TO RESEARCH WORKERS

Research workers vary greatly in their ability to use resources, particularly of staff. Some first-class researchers have difficulty in keeping any assistants employed at all and are unsettled if they have to rely on other people to keep their experimental apparatus going. At the other extreme are researchers not necessarily bright in themselves who can keep a number of programmes going satisfactorily, employing a large number of assistants and large mechanical resources. Efficiency is only obtained where the best use is made of the qualities of the individual research workers. It is therefore important to explore a man's capacity for making effective use of assistants and resources and to plan research programmes so that the maximum use is made of such capacities. Where one has a research worker who is both able in himself and capable of keeping a number of programmes going successfully particular care should be taken to develop him for the widest project tasks.

On the other hand the business of a research worker is to do research and as far as possible he should be relieved from the necessity of dealing with the more routine services allied to his work such as photography, electron/optical microscopy, chemical analysis, glass blowing, machine operation, etc., all of which should, where possible, be provided as a central service.

MEASURING PRODUCTIVITY IN R & D

Efforts to measure productivity in R & D have not proved extremely rewarding. However effective a piece of research is, there is no proof that it could not have been done with less effort and to greater effect. Also whether R & D leads to successful 'paying' innovation can depend as much on market forces as the research itself. In fact there are the two distinct criteria of accomplishment in research. The first is measured scientifically – does the work lead to a noteworthy advance in the frontiers of knowledge? The second is measured 'economically' – does the work lead to an exploitable situation with an ultimate direct value to society? Attempts to measure the first type have sometimes been made, for undoubtedly it is not difficult to recognise that one scientist is superior to another in his scientific ability. A standard way is to measure the output of the scientist in terms of research reports, research notes, technical memoranda, etc., perhaps drawing up a points system and weighting for the different types of report and whether they are published internally or externally. Certainly this method will give a quantitative guide to a quality which is always invoked if only subconsciously in assessing scientists' work, but it is a long way from being accurate, for some scientists will have made greater progress resulting in the publication of a few select reports, while there will be others who are prolific in report writing but whose advances being reported are relatively small. A similar technique has been used by Thomson [63] to compare the universities with government research institutes and industry by comparing the number of Nobel prizewinners for different periods. The results are shown in Table 7.1.

TABLE 7.1   NOBEL PRIZEWINNERS

	1900–1931		1932–1962	
	Names	Prizes	Names	Prizes
Physics				
Universities and teaching institutes	30	$23\frac{1}{2}$	33	$23\frac{1}{2}$
Government and other research institutes	3	3	4	2
Industry	2	$1\frac{1}{2}$	4	$\frac{1}{2}$
Chemistry				
Universities and teaching institutes	26	20	22	$16\frac{1}{2}$
Government and other research institutes	1	1	14	$8\frac{1}{2}$
Industry	2	1	1	1

From this it was fairly concluded that it provides some evidence for the view that conditions for major discoveries are more favourable in the universities than elsewhere, although it is admitted that this may be because the other centres of research do not spend such a high proportion of their time on the sort of research recognised by the Nobel awards.

The effect of organisation size on the productivity of physiologists has been studied by Meltzer and Slater. [64] As measured by numbers of publications, they concluded that scientific productivity was not related to the size of the organisation, but that there was a curvilinear relationship between the size and job satisfaction, being greater in a medium-sized organisation (20-50 employees) than in either smaller or larger organisations. But it is a tenuous conclusion and Meltzer and Slater conclude that other factors are likely to have greater effect than size.

Devising methods of measuring productivity of research where the objective is some 'saleable' product which can somehow be measured in money terms would appear to be easier, though it is doubtful if it is much more rewarding.

The first difficulty arises from the fact that any research department will be conducting some work of an exploratory or background nature which cannot often be directly associated with commercial saleability, although it may give rise to something for which a licensing or patenting fee is obtainable. However, in many departments most of the work will be in aid of some project which either improves existing processes or leads to new products in the widest sense. It is then possible, say, on a yearly basis, to make a complete analysis of all specific programmes terminated during that year and first to judge them as successful if they have led to some beneficial action on the part of the organisation concerned and as a failure if they have not. A second difficulty arises here in that an annual analysis is a rather short time scale for R & D activities and a five-year trend may well be more useful. Where possible an attempt can next be made to quantify the success of the project – by the receipts from royalties or licensing agreements, by the effect on product cost or selling price of an improved process or product, from the increase in profit earned from a newly developed 'product', etc.

The total financial yield of the research is then compared with the total cost of the research function, the non-productive research in this way being treated as an overhead on the productive.

By breaking the costs down into different categories such as the source of new ideas, new processes compared to improving old ones, different groups within the laboratory, etc., some figures can also be obtained for the productivity of different sections of activity for comparative purposes.

This type of analysis can go some way to establishing a type of productivity measurement although since, as we have seen, research is done for many different purposes, one would not necessarily expect a regular high-gain factor on such a measure. In a study carried out at ICI using this type of analysis, it was concluded that positive assurance was obtained that research was paying off and there was a case for expansion rather than contraction of research effort. However, the return was only of the same order as other worthwhile industrial activities. For every £1m spent on research of all kinds, the assessable yield averages around £200,000 per year for say ten years. [65]

Of course R & D has the advantage over other industrial activities that occasionally it can give a fantastically high return.

Indeed one of the dangers of conducting this type of analysis is that it would tend to orient research into that with a high probability of relatively small success over a short time scale, whereas the real objectives of research should be very high-gain factor which tends to mean long time scales and relatively low probability of success.

The measurement of productivity in R & D which is project orientated in the sense described in Chapter 5, where the nature of the overall project largely dictates the research, would be much more difficult. Success is recognised in such a situation by the ability to achieve an end-point, suitable for dovetailing into the project at the time required by the plan, with a minimum of resources. Again, success in this type of activity is recognisable over a period. Some scientists demand large resources, some are always a little later than the plan requires with their solutions and some present their results in a form which requires engineering specification modification to incorporate them. The man, however, who forces the project management to incorporate an acceptable engineering modification, who only uses half the resources to get to that position and gets there just at the time demanded by the master-plan may be obtaining higher productivity than the man who uses the extra resources and gets the perfect answer in ample time.

Such considerations make productivity conceptions apparently impossible to quantify in this project type of situation.

TECHNIQUES FOR THE EFFICIENT USE OF STAFF

In this chapter the problems of making the best use of scientific abilities have rightly come foremost in considering efficiency in R & D.

In the efficient operation of a laboratory, however, we cannot leave out entirely the use of other management techniques such as organisation and method studies in at least the more routine operations where economies of both time and money can be obtained without reducing the effectiveness of the scientific workers.

It is not intended to give much detail of these techniques other than to define them and relate them to R & D activities generally.

ORGANISATION AND METHODS (O & M) SERVICE

This is a service which gives advice on the structure of an organisation, its management and control and its procedure and methods.

It is usually the activity of a group of people within an organisation, set up and trained in the special techniques of O & M for the purpose of examining organisation structures and methods of working wherever in the overall organisation it is considered it might be helpful. It provides a tool to assist the manager with his normal duty to concern himself with organisation and methods, by spending more time and examining in greater depth than a manager normally can for particular sectors where greater efficiency can be anticipated. Normally O & M will systematically review every activity of a unit under study, examining in detail its purpose and the way it functions in order to discover how it can be made to function in a more efficient and economical way.

An O & M review of organisation covers such matters as the division of work, the delegation of authority, the line of authority from the top of an organisation to the bottom, the span of control of individual officers, functional organisation, co-ordination, centralisation v. decentralisation, etc.

Because of the way in which research departments tend to grow in directions away from the original objectives, because scientists do not naturally organise themselves and because services to scientists tend to start in one section and later spread to the others, organisations in research departments can be fruitful studies for O & M experts. They should, however, be experts with some experience in an R & D atmosphere since scientific implications of organisations can easily be lost to those without sympathetic understanding of scientists and their methods.

It is in the structure set up for providing services to scientists that the O & M techniques may prove more useful. An obvious example is the laboratory analytical service which may have grown up in response to requirements of individual scientists without examination of the advantages of centralisation or decentralisation, of grouping like analyses and automating them, of separating analysis research from routine research (and employing appropriate staff) or of improving techniques for carrying out the more common analyses with an eye to reducing the cost.

Similarly the provision of instruments as related to central servicing, use of external maintenance contractors, purchasing of standard types throughout the laboratory, automation to reduce labour, maintaining loan pools on a supply and return basis more cheaply to make available a large range to scientists – all are a fit study for O & M techniques. Of a different type, O & M studies of the administration or management services to the research staff can be useful. The degree of centralisation and decentralisation, how typing services, etc. are most efficiently provided without reducing the services given, the extent of authority allowed to different grades of scientist for purchase of equipment so that freedom and control are best exercised, the planning of transport within a large site. All these matters and many more can provide assistance or irksome frustration to scientists but equally can be exceedingly costly if not planned carefully in accordance with needs. [66]

Staff survey is the examination of work to determine the number of grades of staff required. It is carried out by a team containing at least some members experienced in the techniques of staff survey who examine blocks of activity within an establishment – perhaps a research team, an experimental rig operating team or drawing office – and having assessed that the work being carried out is necessary within the framework of agreed policy, they consider the number and grades of staff needed.

The technique is more suitable in an R & D department for the service elements rather than the research elements themselves, but since service elements like the running of experimental rigs or drawing offices are likely to be affected by changing research project patterns faster than normal management can provide adjustment, it is very valuable in assisting management to adapt to these changing patterns.

So far as application to research teams themselves is concerned, staff survey can be and is applied, but is likely to be more successful where the research is fully project orientated and where the examining body is particularly experienced in the work patterns of research as related to their objectives. It is not, however, unusual to find research activities going on which are not correctly related to the project objective. Other faults that can be discovered include the use of over-high grade scientists for relatively routine research activities, or conversely, the employment of too many assistants who have to be found work relatively useless to the real purpose of the research and thus inhibit the scientist from economically pursuing his true function. [67]

USE AND CONTROL OF LABOUR

Even in the simplest research laboratory it will be found economical to use industrial labour for elementary tasks such as apparatus washing and laboratory cleaning. In large research establishments, where complicated research rigs are operated, complicated apparatus is built and rebuilt, pilot plants are operated and much repeat experimentation is reduced to routine operation, the use of labour occupies an important position in management consideration. From the scientist's point of view the ideal is that men should be available and trained when they are needed for the research programme. He does not wish to be involved in whether they are used efficiently and how they are obtained or trained. However, because of the difficulties of obtaining labour, its cost, problems of adequate pay and training and organisational problems of provision where required in the laboratory, management is becoming increasingly concerned with the efficient control and use of labour in laboratories. In directing a laboratory, skill has to be exercised in trying to effect the best compromise between the interests of the scientist and the efficient management of labour.

An organisational structure is likely to be built up which will follow closely that of the scientific organisation, with each unit in the scientific organisation having its own industrial complement and hierarchy of labour managers, foremen, chargehands, etc., whose function it will be to endeavour to provide trained labour where it is required on an efficient basis. In this way it is more likely that the needs of the scientist will be met with a minimum of interference to him and adequate attention paid to the labour structure. This will vary depending on the nature of the scientific work in relation to the labour-operated services it requires but for project-orientated research with a fair amount of technological equipment 30–60 scientific staff appears to be about the size below which it is difficult to give sufficient flexibility for continuous efficient usage with changing work patterns, and above which the labour organisation is likely to be too impersonal to be closely identified with the scientist's needs.

Where the research establishment itself is of this size, training will require to be partly in-house and will normally be arranged by the foremen, augmented, however, by some external training, perhaps from the training department of the parent organisation of the research department where this is available, or by the use of appropriate education and training institutes where courses on such subjects as laboratory practice, safety and plant operation can be obtained. Equally the foreman and labour managers are likely to be trained in the principles involved in efficient working, such as work study.

Where a research establishment contains many units of this size it is likely to have a training department and efficiency services available within the establishment itself.

Having set up the organisation so that a reasonable degree of efficiency exists in providing the trained labour where it is required by the scientists, and otherwise using it for routine laboratory purposes like cleaning, dismantling unused apparatus, operation of apparatus, stores, etc., the labour management will be faced with the desirability of still further improving the efficiency of the labour force. Pressure to do this is likely to arise either from labour shortages or from union pressure for higher pay, even when the cost margins are not sufficient to justify the interference with the scientist's work pattern which may result. Again the problem of the best compromise between technical efficiency and interference with the scientist's activities is likely to exercise considerable thought.

Further actual efficiency can be achieved in two directions. The first is to upgrade the work which a given worker can do, by further training and exploitation of his best capabilities. In a surprising number of cases, skills can be learnt and successfully applied in areas of work previously considered to be only suitable for scientifically qualified junior staff. If systems of job evaluation (see below) are used or if pay is otherwise geared to contributions, a worker can in this way enjoy a developing wage structure. This, however, will not solve the labour shortage problem if that too exists, and here, improvement in efficiency is to be sought by the use of work study techniques, which, perhaps associated with incentive payments, help to reduce lost time and maintain a comfortable rate of working.

JOB EVALUATION

This is a method of determining the relative standing, for pay purposes, of jobs within an organisation. It can be operated in different ways, for instance:

Ranking – the placing of jobs in order of importance or value as determined by some rough criteria. This is the simplest system but usually only operable in small organisations.

Factor comparison – the analysis, as a basis for comparison, of certain factors for each job, such as skill, mental requirements, physical requirements, responsibility and working conditions. In this system full job descriptions are prepared for certain key jobs and analysed under the factor headings, the pay for each job being apportioned correspondingly. All other jobs are then dealt with by a description being prepared and analysed and pay for each factor being determined by reference to a table of factor rates obtained from the key jobs analysis. [68]

For application to research establishments, job evaluation has the advantage that it deals fairly in the matter of adjusting pay rates with jobs that can have a wide range of combinations of the factors affecting contribution. It has the disadvantage that with rapidly changing work patterns it is necessary to change workers' jobs frequently, and it is difficult to move a man from a job at a high rating to one at a lower rating or to avoid continuous pressure for movement towards higher-rated jobs by workers who have sufficient capability for it.

WORK STUDY

Work study is the general term for those techniques, particularly method study and work measurement which are used in the examination of human work in all its contexts, and which lead systematically to the investigation of all the factors which affect the efficiency and economy of the situation being reviewed, in order to effect improvement. [69]

METHOD STUDY

Method study is probably the most useful of the work study techniques in application to the research environment. It consists of examining a work pattern critically to see whether new ways of doing it might be developed which make it easier, more effective and less costly. While method study uses techniques –

essentially analytical – of the work content of an activity, it can throw up elements of high or difficult labour utilisation which may be overcome by mechanical/electrical means. It does not, however, automatically provide a means of achieving higher work output per man and therefore a basis for higher payment.

WORK MEASUREMENT

Work measurement is the use of techniques which establish the time taken for a qualified worker to carry out a particular job element at a defined level of performance rate. The time that it should take for a complete job can then be built up to establish the amount of work that a given team of workers should carry out in a given time, while working at a standard rate, and form a basis for incentive payments based on their actual rate of working.

It is not easy to apply such techniques to research laboratory working. The work patterns tend to change continually and to be substantially altered before a work-studied operation has settled down: research exercise has inevitably to suffer some distortion because of the pressure to keep workers supplied with work at their rate of working. It can, however, be operated where necessary making use particularly of synthetic work study in which the elements of a new job are timed on the basis of experience with similar elements of previous experience. In such a case operations can be carried out on a work-studied basis from their commencement. Also, since in any laboratory there are routine operations not directly connected with research work, such jobs can be work studied more easily and can be used to occupy the workers' time when direct assistance to the scientist is not required.

In many laboratories much of the equipment upon which research is done – experimental nuclear reactors, particle accelerators, test machines – can in fact be operated on a fairly routine basis so far as the operators are concerned, although new experiments are in fact continually being performed in them. In such cases work study techniques are satisfactory for maintaining operating teams at a high rate of working. Since such facilities usually have a backlog of experiments waiting to be carried out, there is not such a problem of filling in the non-operational time.

ACTIVITY SAMPLING

This is a technique in which a large number of instantaneous observations are made, over a period of time, of a group of machines, processes or workers. [69]

Each observation records what is happening at the instant of the observation and then the percentage of observations recorded for a particular activity (or absence of activity) indicates the percentage of time during which that activity (or absence of activity) occurs. In such an analysis one might find in an apparently well-organised laboratory that one third of the workers' time is spent on fetching stores, taking messages or miscellaneous administrative matters, one third on the actual experimentation and one third doing nothing. Such data enable the foreman or managers to take steps to reduce or eliminate the non-productive time. This is a very useful technique for research establishments since it is difficult for a management mainly concerned with supervising research activities to become aware of the hindrances to smooth working that build up in an organisation at industrial level. Also it is an activity that can be carried out to a significant extent, without highly developed specialised skills, by foremen or junior managers.

ENGINEERING SERVICES

It is almost axiomatic that scientists do not find engineering services satisfactory. In the day-to-day conduct of research the scientist wants all the equipment that his researches lead him to wish for and he wants it immediately. He also wants the engineering resources that his overall research plan calls for at the times demanded by the network based on the research plan, and not at the times that the engineering services could conveniently supply it. He wants engineers and draughtsmen immediately available to interpret his experimental requirements into hardware and he does not want engineers interfering with his equipment for routine maintenance. If it does break down, he wants immediate repair, but he does not want fitters around otherwise.

So engineering services are always set an impossible task by scientists. Indeed, it is just as well that they are, for good scientists can always create ideas for new apparatus beyond their resources to operate. Limited engineering is, therefore, one control which directs scientists into choosing economically the experiments (particularly expensive ones) which really count towards the objective.

The correct balance and organisation of engineering services is, therefore, a most important consideration in the efficient operation of R & D. Undoubtedly research teams need some direct engineering resources for servicing their equipment, building the simpler apparatus quickly and without formality and for preliminary discussions on the engineering implications of the research leads. Care has to be taken that these directly available engineering resources are adequate in quantity and type to be fully utilised by the research team, so that the scientist is not impeded in obtaining essential apparatus reasonably quickly, but not so great that work has to be invented for them or demands not really necessary are placed on them. But for major, expensive equipment it will generally be more economic to use a more formal engineering organisation in which specifications and engineering drawings are produced, costing estimated, approval given at the appropriate level, and manufacture considered and controlled in relation to central manufacturing arrangements. The necessity of specification and drawing will go a long way to ensuring that the scientist gets the equipment he wishes and not an incorrect engineering interpretation of it. A costing and approval process will ensure that expensive equipment is only entertained in relation to an overall research plan and budgeting considerations. Equally, if new ideas have reached a stage where major resources are required to take them further it may have become necessary to reconsider the overall research plan and, indeed, the budgeting for it.

Similarly general maintenance of equipment and services is best carried out by a central engineering department rather than by engineers assigned to scientists, for then the best principles of maintenance practice and efficiency considerations can be applied in an area in which the scientist is not greatly interested. Maintenance schedules of specialised equipment on the other hand should be reviewed by the scientists concerned as they are more likely to know the points of likely failure and where failure is likely to be most unacceptable for operating or hazard reasons. However, the operation of large experimental rigs, such as experimental nuclear reactors, complicated heat transfer rigs or inert atmosphere plants, may be so integrated with the experimental work carried out on them that the experimental team has to be in direct charge of the engineering operation.

It will thus be clear that the careful organisation of engineering services can play an important part in the efficiency and productivity of a research establishment, well beyond the implementation of efficiency techniques directly applied to these services themselves.

USING THE AVAILABLE SYSTEM

While management can consider all these methods of increasing the efficiency of research activity, they will only be effective if they are made use of by the research staff at all appropriate levels, preferably in a spirit of enthusiastic co-operation. Ideally the scientist himself will perform only a minimum amount of the most highly skilled experimentation, making use of the services available to him for designing and building his equipment, operating it, simple analysis of results, computer usage, organising labour and supplies, arranging contracts, etc.

Scientists will only conform to these ideals if they are aware of the advantages which using the system available to them will confer and are well trained in its use. Scientists are indeed very variable in their abilities to use the resources available to them but it is an important function of management, by communication in various ways, to achieve the maximum usage of the system by its scientists.

SUMMARY

In considering efficiency and productivity in the research field it must be remembered that enhancing scientific quality and conserving the time and energy of the research workers will give the greatest contribution and should always be considered first in mounting efficiency exercises.

The effect of control levels on research effectiveness is for instance a difficult subject and there is a tendency for numbers of higher echelons to be more effective in mission-orientated research.

Economy of experimentation is a considerable source of improved productivity, and the fewest possible experiments should be done in direct line to the project requirement, with well characterised conditions, only when adequate knowledge or theory are not available, and at the correct scale. The best instrumentation, automatic operation and computerisation should be available to the extent that it provides maximum help in experimentation and does not waste time. The best tools that a laboratory can afford will pay rewards in depth of scientific attack and in attracting the best scientists.

Measuring productivity is not very rewarding but some attempts at this are described.

After the efficiency of the scientific worker has been maximised, one will probably be forced, because of labour difficulties and restriction of resources, to consider aids to efficiency of other aspects of the laboratory.

The use of organisation and methods, staff survey, job evaluation, method study, work measurement, activity sampling are all techniques which find a place in modern large laboratories. The efficiency of engineering services in relation to research is also important and, finally, greatest output will be obtained from scientists who are taught and are receptive to the maximum use of the resources that are available to them.

8 Staff selection, development and management

RECRUITMENT AND PROMOTION

Irrespective of the type of research to be undertaken its success will depend more than anything on the quality of the scientific staff. Not all scientists and engineers, even though well qualified, are suitable for research and development efforts. People have to be selected who offer the highest probability of creating new ideas and who at the same time are capable of working without close supervision in fields where few facts are available. Probably the vital ingredients for success in a scientist are curiosity and initiative and an urge to improve everything he comes into contact with. He is likely to have a good education and must have above average intelligence. He must know his subject in a professional manner and be able to apply his talents to it and he must have an urge to accomplish something. Enthusiasm is a great asset, though many researchers achieve results with an attitude that appears to fall short of enthusiasm.

It is fortunately only rarely that the necessity arises of recruiting a complete laboratory establishment in one step. The more usual exercise is to recruit in accordance with the small year-by-year changes in the research portfolio, as the work of the establishment expands, or in a more static situation as replacement of wastage becomes necessary. In considering the appointment of staff, two things are of first importance. The first is to fix the level of operation – whether one is looking for a section leader or a group leader, a research worker or an experimental assistant – for it is important for the needs of a project and the healthy working of a team as a whole that a sound balance is obtained between the different levels of operation. The existence of numbers of young and inexperienced workers, operating without appropriately experienced section leaders above them and group leaders to manage the overall plan, is likely seriously to reduce the power of the team to achieve planned objectives. Equally, unless section leaders have younger, less experienced research officers to work with them, output of good section leaders is likely to be seriously limited. Equally the correct balance between research scientists and lesser-graded experimental assistants needs to be carefully considered. There is no single suitable ratio, for it depends on how much experimental compared with theoretical work needs to be done and the extent to which large experimental equipment needs to be operated. A ratio of about 2.5:1 (experimental assistants: research officers) is, however, an average sort of figure, as found in the Scientific Civil Service.

Unfortunately the ability to maintain 'correct' balances of these types can be thrown off-course by overall laboratory policies relating to the size and scope of a laboratory's activities, and provides one reason why the size and operation of a research establishment should be modified only gradually if at all possible (see p. 167).

Having decided just which posts need to be filled it is next desirable to consider very carefully a specification for each post available – what basic discipline is required, what general experience and any special additional expertise or qualification, the degree of theoretical or practical ability that is required – and it is a worthwhile exercise to write out such a specification carefully; this is particularly true if the recruitment is not to be carried out by the section which is to use the man. It too often happens that graduates, particularly young graduates from universities, are recruited without much attention being given to their particular suitability to the tasks involved, which leads to frustration and failure. A particular aspect of the specification that requires attention is whether the post is to be in a near free research field or project orientated and carefully to recruit accordingly. It is usually easier to recruit the type of man who wishes to conduct pure research work because that is the experience he will have had at the university. For project-orientated work recruitment is more difficult, but what has chiefly to be avoided is appointment of lower qualified people who may feel that pure research is beyond them but that project-orientated research is a less difficult discipline. The objective in recruiting for project-orientated research should be to obtain the best quality staff possible, but including those who recognise the value of the additional challenges which good project-orientated work offers.

On the other hand there are many tasks at the development end of the R & D spectrum where a research training or even a degree is less important than an aptitude for combining scientific knowledge with engineering-type thinking and for which the correct choice may well be HNC or similarly qualified staff. The recruitment of graduates – especially PhDs – purely for prestige reasons has no place in a modern R & D department.

It may not prove possible actually to recruit as closely to the specification as one wishes, and where an appreciable disparity exists it may be necessary to review the staff structure in relation to the research portfolio, to see whether moves can be made to fit the best candidates to a new arrangement.

Recruiting is a creative job in itself and it is advisable that senior research and development staff members should be closely associated with it – directly in the interviewing of prospective staff if at all possible, and certainly in the case of graduate recruitment from universities, and in the creation of contacts with university departments which are appropriate recruiting grounds. Arming the recruiting personnel with brochures, etc., describing the nature of the recruiting organisation, to give to prospective recruits is useful so long as they represent a genuine attempt to describe the nature of the environment the recruits will work in, rather than give an impressive sales talk on the organisation's projects. For it is as important that a recruit should think the employing environment is suitable for him, as for the employer to think the recruit is suitable.

Care should always be taken to ensure that newcomers have a definite place in the team and a definite function to perform. Particularly with young graduates, there is a tendency to care little what they do for the first few months so that they can 'find their feet'. While such a process is necessary, it should not be done in an aimless fashion and if there is no immediate need for full integration into a team, then a project should be designed, relative to the objectives of the laboratory for which they should be responsible.

Whatever experience a recruit has had, entering a new environment presents him with new problems and some positive training steps should always be taken to enable him to understand the general nature of the activities of the laboratory, the general pattern of administration of services and the resources that are available to him and how he can make use of them. The arrangements for safety control should be particularly described at an early date.

Having established the right man in the right job at the beginning of his career with an organisation, care must be taken, particularly in the early years that arrangements should be made to monitor his initial progress. Frequently this is carried out by some formal assessment practice in which his aptitude for different elements in his work are marked or commented on every six months or year. This may or may not be complemented by discussion with the man on his progress, but certainly it is undesirable to accept indifferent marking or comments by a man's immediate supervisors without instituting some enquiries as to whether the man is correctly placed in a congenial atmosphere. It is all too common an experience to find a man condemned by one superior office prove to be extremely able under different circumstances where the job is more suited to a man's abilities. Sometimes a temperamental clash occurs and this is to be avoided, or corrected, so far as possible by someone at senior level being involved in discussions with new staff at the early stages in their career.

In large organisations the promotion of staff can cause some complicated problems. Allowing that promotion is likely to be an aim of considerable importance to most staff, both for the extra salary it is likely to earn, and perhaps more importantly so that a man can satisfactorily match himself against his fellows, it will need to be considered in the light of:

(a) Standards of performance required should be accepted as uniform and fair by both the man and his colleagues, both in relation to employment inside a given research establishment and outside it.

(b) In the processes of promotion some degree of impartiality should be seen to operate, rather than complete dependence on the views of immediate superior officers.

(c) The performance required for promotion should be related to the type of work that a man is required to do. Thus a man who is expected to complete a difficult project objective should not be judged by the quality of the scientific reports he has written.

(d) The structural requirements of the department are inevitably taken into account when deciding what posts are available for promotion, but we should also bear in mind the ability of some good scientists to make excellent contributions without a lot of staff, and the concept of having an avenue open for the best scientists to be able to operate at very high level on a personal basis should be observed. Temporary structural appearances should not, therefore, intrude too much into the promotion pattern at the research working levels.

Many schemes for promotion procedures can be envisaged which take these considerations into effect, but an interviewing panel which has some members on it of scientific reputation from outside the department, and which takes careful account of the nature of the work and the views of supervising staff at different levels, as well as the reactions of the interviewed staff, would appear to be a simple but effective method.

STAFF DEVELOPMENT

The principal raw material being fed into a research department is the graduate but he requires a good deal of processing before he is fully productive to the limit of his capability. This development of staff to realise their full potential is of great importance in maximising the performance of a laboratory – and deserves careful attention.

There are three directions in which staff development can be undertaken:

(a) To improve performance as a scientist, particularly where applicable, as a project-orientated practitioner and to enlarge knowledge in relevant fields.
(b) To develop any particular cross-disciplinary expertise, e.g. materials engineering, which may be of particular interest in the laboratory.
(c) To develop managerial abilities to fit a person for later section leader and research manager posts.

TO IMPROVE PERFORMANCE AS A SCIENTIST/TECHNOLOGIST

In the practice of basic or exploratory science, development is likely to occur most quickly by associating the scientist with more experienced scientists – in the widest sense. Not only should a less experienced scientist be working directly for a more experienced scientist under conditions of mutual respect, but areas of contact should be widened by frequent association with specialists in the appropriate field in the universities or other major research centres, and by attendances at appropriate scientific conferences, without limiting the field of such contacts on too narrow a basis, but equally without expecting the scientists – or supporting requests from him – to attend conferences not remotely connected with the field being worked in. The cross-fertilisation that comes from mixing disciplines should be particularly encouraged so that chemists might be encouraged to explore associated fields in physics, mathematics, or appropriate technologies.

By far the greater amount of research being carried out nowadays, however, is project orientated or of development type. In such work the ability to do good research work is not sufficient, although it is necessary and the same efforts at staff development are required as for basic research. Additional is the requirement of experience with systematic techniques (some of which have been discussed in previous chapters) which can both expedite the work and reduce its cost, and which serve to assist in promoting the sense of urgency and creation of an object (engineering) which are essential to project-orientated research. Table 8.1 reviews some of the techniques which might assist the project operator. [5]

The development of scientists towards project operation is surprisingly not at present being given a great deal of attention and strenuous efforts appear to have so far failed to persuade universities to mount courses for this purpose. Steps are therefore necessary by means of internal training, encouragement in practising such techniques or short lecture courses, to bridge this important gap in the average scientist's training. Attendance at one of the few courses operated by the private management training organisations should also be given consideration.

TO DEVELOP PARTICULAR CROSS-DISCIPLINARY EXPERTISE

As has been mentioned before much successful research work, particularly as applied to practical problems, occurs in areas associated with a mixture of disciplines, whereas it remains largely true that graduates are trained in a single limited discipline that can be named chemistry or physics or some such subject.

An example of this has occurred in recent years in the development of materials science as a subject which arose because of the general recognition of the importance of materials in modern technology. Although a chemist would know something about plastics, a metallurgist about metals and a civil engineer about concrete, modern usage demanded not only a knowledge of all types of materials but also their general and specific properties in physical terms, and modern technological materials problems needed to be solved by those who were equally at home with many different species of materials and with the problems of their properties particularly in association with each other (as in composites). The development of materials science teaching has helped to widen this concept usefully. This, however, is now being found to be insufficient and because a material is only of value if it can be made into a useful object, problems of engineering to make the best use of materials in complete structures intrude. The concept of a materials engineer is, therefore, growing up with the job of designing and creating new and improved materials

TABLE 8.1 REVIEW OF TECHNIQUES IN PROJECT OPERATION

Technique	Purpose	Application	Advantages	Drawbacks
METHOD STUDY	Simplification and improvement of working methods	All work, either manual or mental	No mathematics; easily understood by layman	Deceptively simple; experience needed for best results
FORMAL CRITICAL EXAMINATION: PABLA	Improvements of plans and projects	Flow sheets, programmes engineering designs	No mathematics; it can be a patent stimulus to original thinking	Deceptively simple; experience needed for best results
NETWORK ANALYSIS OR CRITICAL PATH PLANNING	Programming for minimum project time	All projects made up of activities whose duration can be estimated	Simple arithmetic; clear visual representation	Input data (job times etc.) are often highly uncertain
RESOURCE ALLOCATION	Economy and effectiveness in use of staff, labour and equipment	Projects for which a network has been drawn up	Simple graphical techniques; correct the network to allow for scarce resources	Input data are often highly uncertain
OPTIMISATION	A general term covering all quantitative techniques for determining optimum solutions to problems	Processes and operations in which the desired objective can be stated as a number	Quantitative solutions replace or supplement subjective hunches	Unless reliable input data are available, optimisation techniques are misleading
LINEAR AND NON-LINEAR PROGRAMMING	Finding the best solution of complex problems involving numerous variables	Conduct of large projects and extensive operations	Provides quantitative solutions of problems which were formerly too complex for analysis	Simple mathematical equations for the system must be known or assumed. If these are in error so is the solution
STATISTICAL DESIGN	Economy of time and effort in experimentation	Projects involving large numbers of experiments or observations	A well-proved technique for which reliable mathematical methods are available	May render an experimental programme somewhat inflexible
MATHEMATICAL SIMULATION	To predict the behaviour of a physical system (plant process or machine) on paper	Any system for which the relevant differential equations are known	Quicker and cheaper than the physical experimentation especially with a computer	It is never quite certain that the known differential equations completely describe the system
PHYSICAL SIMULATION	To reproduce the behaviour of a large system by experimenting with a	Physical system for which the differential equations are incompletely known	Results usually more reliable than those obtained on paper. Product sam-	More costly and time-consuming than calculated: results occasion-

systems and organising the development and implementation of these to the point of efficient phasing into production or machine construction – based on materials sciences, engineering sciences and management sciences. Efforts are being made to develop courses at universities for such materials engineers. [70]

With the highly sophisticated materials systems required for aerospace, nuclear energy and similar modern technologies, the development of materials physicists who can analyse the effect of interchange of energy of different forms with materials, or even materials mathematicians has equally become of importance.

The problems, therefore, of staff development from the raw material of graduates in simple disciplines can be a formidable one: the materials field is of course only one example of a situation that occurs in many modern technological developments. Probably the most effective way of dealing with it is to compose teams of mixed disciplines, such as putting research-minded engineers directly into a materials research team, and to back this up with attendance at short training courses on subjects in the 'unknown' discipline. It has not been found fully successful for the staff of different disciplines to operate from different functional divisions when problems are very firmly dependent on the interaction of more than one discipline for success.

TO DEVELOP MANAGERIAL ABILITIES

The development of staff in such a direction that they can aspire to posts as section leader, and eventually perhaps research manager, is also of considerable value in maintaining a healthy department, for in general promotions from within a department are to be preferred to the necessity, sometimes unavoidable, of seeking to fill supervisory posts from outside. This must be carried out by assessing staff at all levels for their capacity for further responsibility; such capacity should also be encouraged by arranging for them to assume extra supervisory responsibility and moving them into situations where their experience will be widened, particularly in the necessity of utilising wide-ranging resources to carry out their duties.

Cost consciousness has also to be introduced at an early stage in the development of research managers, for finance is both a resource and a constraint that the research manager has to work with.

TEMPORARY V. PERMANENT STAFF

For stability and progression a research department will usually be staffed by 'permanent' employees, i.e. employees with reasonable security against unexpected dismissal. There is, however, a place of value in a research establishment for the temporary employment of staff, particularly of specialised scientists of high reputation, for the stimulus that it might give to the more permanent staff and the widening of scientific horizons in the work of the department. Where suitable, therefore, it can be very fruitful to employ a university or research association scientist for a short spell in a more project-orientated laboratory as an intermission in his normal activity.

MANAGEMENT OF STAFF IN R & D ENVIRONMENT

ORGANIC ORGANISATION

While we have seen that large R & D organisations are likely to be structured on a hierarchical basis (Chapter 3) the actual management of R & D staff is developing a new orientation departing radically from the traditional bureaucratic patterns associated with hierarchical organisations.

The central emphases in this development are:

1. Wide participation in decision making, rather than centralised decision making.
2. The face-to-face group rather than the individual issuing instructions.
3. Mutual confidence rather than authority as the integrative force in the organisation.
4. The supervisor as the agent for maintaining intra-group and inter-group communication rather than as the agent of higher authority.
5. Growth of members of the organisation to greater re-

sponsibility rather than external control of the member's performance of their tasks.

On the surface this may appear to be exercising the soft option but, particularly where large projects are concerned, it demands greater effort on the part of both 'managers' and 'managed'.

The organisation which typically has these elements has been described by Burns [71] as 'organic' and a good deal of study has been put into it. In considering this type of organisation Knight [35] suggests that it is in accord with the following characteristics that may be assigned to creative staff.

1. Creative problem solving appears to be a high-risk activity that is often erratic and unpredictable.

2. Creative people appear to have a detached devotion to their work; they have a deep commitment to the problem that they are trying to solve, yet they are not so deeply immersed that they are unable to see the problem in a broader perspective.

3. Creative people are receptive to all kinds of ideas. They will consider them and judge them on their merits.

4. Creative people rely on free exploration in that they actively go out and search for new alternatives, advice, ideas and opinions from a wide variety of sources.

5. Creative individuals appear to commit themselves to a specific solution to their problems later than their less creative counterparts.

6. Creative people tend to be non-conformists and question authority and existing problem solutions.

7. Perhaps the most outstanding characteristic of creative people is a confidence to question authority and a strong drive to pursue their own ideas and proposals.

This is perhaps an idealised picture of the creative scientist, and it should be noted that in any research department there will be many scientists who are performing less creative duties and who could well function competently in organisations of a more authoritarian type.

But these considerations possess important implications for an organisation seeking to stimulate invention, both regarding its selection policies and its style of managing creative staff.

The more negative attributes of scientists need also to be considered. Technical and research people are often in the first place not skilled in establishing good personal relationships with colleagues in other areas of work. Failure to relate satisfactorily may lead to an experience of anxiety, feelings of not being appreciated, of low self-esteem and the like. This leads to their becoming less effective as problem solvers. If a substantial proportion of the staff of a department move in this direction (and this is quite possible) their lack of success will cause greater constraints, financial and otherwise, to be put on them by the parent authority which will exacerbate their condition still further. It may be argued that the only way to untie a knot of this kind must lie in the general direction of an attempt to increase the familiarity and understanding of activities as between different sections of the organisation.

This, it will be noted, may be claimed to be more likely to happen in the 'organic' model of organisational operation where close co-operation is always encouraged and is vital to the successful adaptation to rapid change.

ORGANISATION AND FREEDOM

This must not be interpreted as meaning that controls, clearcut objectives, valid evaluation procedures and organisation are not essential in order successfully to administer large research and project organisations.

Bronowski has said that J. J. Thompson, who hovered between chaos and anarchy all his life, had said that he took great pleasure when during the war he worked with and under men of a different outlook. A problem would be posed with four or five possible lines of approach. One line would be selected and he was always astonished and refreshed by the results of this method of direct regimentation of research.

Again, however, organisation itself within a research institution should be as flexible as possible and even the structure of staff groupings should be regarded as little more than an administrative convenience. For it is impossible to preduct the course that will be followed in research on a complicated problem, and the team organisation set up to do a job at its beginning may not be a suitable one for later stages of its development.

MOTIVATING FACTORS FOR SCIENTIFIC STAFF

That staff of any sort cannot be correctly considered as being motivated by purely salary considerations has been recently increasingly recognised in all work fields. This is particularly true of scientists who, although as interested in salaries relative to their colleagues as the next man, also need other satisfactions. There have been various studies of needs, motivation and morale factors in work situations in recent years. Basically a worker's needs are for:

> rewards
> satisfying work
> responsibility
> good work conditions
> status in relation to his fellows.

Strong awareness of a need will motivate a man towards satisfying it. It would follow that the recognition of these needs and arranging so that a man can aim to achieve them by fulfilling the research aims should provide motivation towards higher productivity. It would equally follow that the complete satisfaction of needs is undesirable as no incentive would remain to work for any purpose. A certain degree of conflict is, therefore, a desirable state and there is much evidence to suggest that scientists in particular are energetic where they are aiming for personal objectives rather than fulfilling them. One study carried out on a medium-sized Central Electricity Generating Board laboratory of 92 people, 18 of whom had honours degrees, drew the conclusions:

(a) Strongly felt needs
Good wages or salary (relative to outside rates)
Good leave entitlement
Opportunity for growth and advancement
Improvement of skill or ability
Jobs which one can be proud to accomplish and which earn the recognition of professional equals

Interesting work under outstanding research leadership and guidance

Good laboratory, office or workshop and equipment

Efficient work planning, giving freedom from non-scientific work

Weakly felt needs

Initial fringe benefits

Status

Appreciation of job accomplishments by outside professional colleagues

Freedom from enforced overtime and overnight stays

Some freedom to choose jobs

Sports and social meetings

Well defined work

A knowledge of weakly-felt needs should prevent management effort being wasted in these areas.

(b) The scientific staff were among those who felt those needs most strongly and were the least satisfied that they were being met: their supervisors were the most satisfied.

(c) The attempt was made to increase work motivation by dealing with the strongly-expressed needs and the productivity response (measured in numbers of reports) gave trends which were said to be encouraging. [72]

A general conclusion on providing incentives for research workers is that they should be faced with challenging problems which require a little more depth or width than obtains in their experience to date, and with enough content fully to extend them; that they should see that successful solution to such problems puts them in line for advancement consideration and that their conditions of working should be good. They should be able to obtain the resources they need – modern equipment, assistants to their capacity for dealing with them and ability to obtain training suitable to their tasks and ambitions – although none of these things should be provided too easily except against proven accomplishment, and where further aims are extant.

POWER AND CONFLICT WITHIN ORGANISATIONS

In considering the place of staff in research organisations, some reference should be made to recent studies on the place of power and conflict in large organisations, for these are processes with which we have to contend.

Power relations within an organisation are never so clarified as reference to a simple structural diagram which gives the superficial statement of levels of authority would suggest. The power structure is in fact much more complicated. Firstly, it has to be remembered that it is a reciprocal relationship involving force or coercion on the one side but voluntary compliance on the other. [73] It may be exercised in many different ways. There is legitimate power – the obvious type conferred by the hierarchical structure – charismatic or referent authority, in which power is conceded by force of personality, and expert power, based on the special knowledge or intellectual superiority of one person compared with another. Charismatic and expert authority can be disruptive in an organisation unless held in some relationship with the organisational structure, but they have a place particularly in research organisations where simple coercive power is not very acceptable to the types of personnel involved.

Apart from personal power developments one also finds inter-departmental power differentials which may be constructive or disruptive depending on the extent to which they serve the ultimate aims of the organisation.

Conflict can arise in an organisation from any of these lateral power relationships or indeed between the structural levels where the balance of compliance and conferred power is not stable.

Conflict can also arise from the interaction of staff, with professional allegiance, and the organisation, with its larger goals, and this is a particularly formidable force in the operation of research establishments. [74] Because of these larger allegiances the research worker is less likely to accept the aims of an organisation without reference to the alternative aims of his profession and also society itself. The control of such staff through a hierarchy which is of an administrative type bound severely to the understood goals of the organisation is very difficult. If control is given to a scientist there is still uncertainty as to whether the scientists are contributing adequately to the goals of the organisation.

The dilemma is frequently resolved by allowing the scientists largely to control themselves, with a fellow scientist (for example, the research director) held accountable for the work of the unit as a whole. It follows that the research director has the task of smoothing this particular conflict but satisfying himself that the goals of the parent authority are being met.

This type of lateral power relationship, however, remains a difficult area in organisations like industry, where alienation exists between those who think scientists impractical in relation to the goals of the firm and the scientists who think the organisation too short-sighted.

Another type of lateral relationship difficulty is where experts of different types take different views on which is the best procedure. The perspectives of accountants, lawyers, scientists, training experts, marketing consultants are unlikely easily to produce consensus views and the bigger the organisation and the greater the proliferation of specialists the more is such conflict inevitable.

Another danger to the effective operation of a large organisation is the development of 'cliques' which can take place across organisational lines and can have vertical and horizontal elements. Such cliques can form for common defence against real or imagined threats and are not likely to be anything but disruptive of the effective working of the organisation, although they represent forces which need to be taken into account in formulating goals.

The power of relatively lowly participants in an organisation has also to be taken into account. A personal secretary is capable of frustrating the working of an office, and laboratory assistants can make scientists dependent on them.

Dalton views an organisation as 'a bewildering mosaic of swiftly-changing and conflicting cliques which cut across departmental and traditional loyalties'.

In a well-run organisation this is likely to be an exaggeration, but undoubtedly organisations act with a consistent interplay of power variables which belie the simplicity of structure diagrams.

This interplay of power variables produces an equally elaborate field of conflicts which are not a problem of awkward individuals, although individuals may highlight the conflicts that exist for organisational reasons.

Other sources of conflict include:

(a) Where different sub-units in organisations perform tasks that come into conflict because they are basically incompatible. The example of scientific and engineering departments in research establishments is a well-known one (see page 219).

(b) If sub-units have similar functions either hostile rivalry or good-natured competition can result. This occurs in a research establishment, for instance, where two or more sections can offer solutions to parts of a technological programme. In the sense that this gives a valuable choice to the project organiser, this is beneficial to the organisation. In the sense that effort may be wasted while each section plays its own solution unmercifully and apportions resources unreasonably, it is destructive. It is desirable that there should be mechanisms for strong and well-judged resolution of such conflicts built into the organisation.

(c) Hierarchical struggles over subtle organisational rewards, status and prestige with the lower levels trying to improve themselves by acting against the more privileged. In a research establishment this represents a continuous source of friction, particularly between administration and scientific divisions. Its resolution, as so often happens, by giving way to the scientist can be a cause of intense frustration to the administration.

Organisations do and have need to develop mechanisms to resolve or control conflicts of all types. This may be in the form of a 'side payment' in terms of prestige or influence, or the allocation of other interesting work, it may be by bringing higher coercive forces into play (appealing to higher and higher levels in the hierarchy), or it may be by having the offices of mediatorship written into tasks at appropriate levels, and choosing staff with the appropriate mediating qualities at potential trouble spots. This latter is undoubtedly the best, although the least practised, for conflicts are not easily resolved without an aftermath which may form the seat of new conflict.

Thus the contemporary view of conflict in an organisation is that it is not inherently bad or good. Power and conflict are major re-shapers of the state of an organisation and can be disruptive if not dealt with effectively but constructive if understood and allowed to condition the correct re-shaping activity. [75]

The problems of staff selection, development and management are thus vital to the operation of a research department – more so than in most industrial/economic undertakings because of the special qualities and the high importance of the scientists concerned. Too often they are tackled in an uninformed and unimaginative way and do not form a subject of training courses for research management as much as they deserve.

SUMMARY

The recruiting of scientific staff is an important task which should exercise to some extent all management levels. The vital characteristics of good research workers or development technologists must be considered, the nature of the post to be filled and the correct balance of scientists to their assistants.

The care of new graduates in an organisation is also an important task.

Promotion opportunities and methods used in an R & D department must encourage high scientific standards but also the ability to accomplish project objectives. It must be seen to be fair and as impartial as possible.

The development of existing staff to its maximum potential in three directions is important

(a) to improve performance as a scientist – particularly for a project-orientated practitioner: some of the techniques which should be taught are considered.

(b) to develop particular cross disciplinary expertise: the examples of materials science and materials engineering are discussed.

(c) to develop managerial abilities.

Elements of the type of organisation most conducive to the flowering of scientific thought are described in relation to the characteristics that may be assigned to scientific staff.

Motivating factors, particularly applicable to scientific staff, including pride in accomplishment, requirement of good scientific leadership, good equipment and scientific facilities, and recognition of professional equals are analysed.

The greatest motivation for scientific staff is to face them with challenging problems always a little more difficult than they have hitherto experienced.

According to contemporary views of conflict in an organisation where it arises in relation to the power structure of the organisation and its causes, conflict is a major re-shaper of organisations which can be constructive if understood and acted upon.

9 Laboratory planning and administration

Perhaps the era of greatest expansion in laboratory building which started in the 1950s is now receding. Laboratories are now less likely to be regarded as symbols of prestige and growth, and cost consciousness makes the careful optimisation of use of existing laboratory buildings a first consideration.

Nevertheless most scientists at managing levels will at some time be involved in the planning of a new laboratory or the major extension of an old one. Such a task is usually tackled with enthusiasm and pride, and most scientists will have some prejudices and some knowledge of the deficiencies they have experienced in other laboratories, but the successful planning of a major laboratory project requires a more solid foundation. There is a sense in which only the occupant of a laboratory knows what he wants – in terms of how many people are to work there, what is the basic type of work to be done, what special facilities are required, what degrees of flexibility and what special services. This cannot be stated without a carefully thought exercise being mounted. Equally when the occupants' requirements have been stated it requires a great deal of specialised engineering and architectural skill to translate such requirements firstly into plant, equipment and technical solutions to service run problems, and then to compose them in relation to space requirements into an harmonious architectural whole. [76]

GENERAL PLANNING

A laboratory project will probably start with the parent authority having convinced itself, or become convinced, that there is a need for a new laboratory building. The conviction might have arisen from a case that the laboratory director has prepared relating to the research programme agreed, or it might have arisen from some higher policy decision brought about by forces external to the laboratory – a decision of the parent authority to diversify into new fields, the fact that a rival organisation has just built a new laboratory, or the space occupied by the existing laboratory becoming so valuable or so inconvenient that it will be advantageous to set up a new laboratory elsewhere. In any case a first requirement will be to frame a rough plan upon which a first cost estimate can be made, for except where the need for the new laboratory is so paramount and urgent that cost does not matter (as can occur with, for example, defence laboratories concerned with urgent national priorities) it is likely that the parent authority will wish to limit the budget in some way.

It will be the research director's job to produce this first plan and he will probably discharge it by setting up a small working party which is likely to remain in existence throughout the building period. It should be well chosen and criteria for membership should include:

(a) Each member to have sufficient standing in the organisation to command co-operation from those from whom information is to be obtained.

(b) Members should include a representative of the eventual operating section and the scientists who will eventually be in residence, if these are different, and also an engineer with some laboratory building experience.

(c) There should be a member, probably the chairman, representing a broad management view.

(d) All members must be able to devote adequate time to their task and not have to regard it as something to be fitted in when they are not too busy elsewhere.

The first task of this committee will be to produce a functional specification which will be a statement in general terms of what is thought to be needed. A typical list of questions to be answered at this point would be as follows:

Functional specification of new building

1. Brief description of building, saying what it is to be used for, particularly if there are any special features such as explosives, radioactivity or high pressure operations – whether basic laboratory type or prototype/pilot plant buildings, whether flexibility for future rearrangement is required.

2. *Block layout* Sizes of different laboratory types and known ancilliary requirements such as offices, changing rooms and wash rooms, photographic facilities, conference space, library, canteens, first-aid/medical/health/physics facilities, security control buildings, general administration.

3. *Occupancy* Numbers of staff, male or female and grades relative to office occupancy and sizes, number of operatives and what facilities they require, such as locker rooms.

4. *Services*
   (a) Piped services. Cold water, chilled water, hot water, distilled water, gas, high pressure air, vacuum, nitrogen, argon, oxygen, laboratory washes, clear water drains.
   (b) Electrical, single phase, three phase, extra low voltage, sockets for equipment.
   (c) Hood exhaust – total area and face velocities.

5. *Special services* Radioactivity, clean rooms, ventilation, air conditioning, controlled temperature/humidity rooms, dry rooms, shielding for criticality, animal rooms for medical or biological work, special fire fighting, fire and radiation warning systems, central air sampling, special lighting, controls and alarms, emergency electricity, security, safety showers and eye washes.

6. *Installed equipment* Cranes, lifts, machine tools, laboratory furniture, special experimental equipment such as wind tunnels, chambers, explosion chambers, sterilisation, photographic darkrooms.

7. *Special installation features* Vibration supports required for precision equipment; positioning and installation of balance rooms and balances; glass blowing and mechanical services rooms, heavy moving equipment foun-

dations, explosion hazard equipment requiring protection and remote control, optical and spectrographic equipment, shielding for radioactive counters.

8. *Special features* Room heights, floor and wall finishes, roof usage, double glazing, architectural fitments.

9. Road approaches, car parking.

With such a functional specification, if drawn up carefully, it is likely that the engineer on the working party will be able to derive a first estimate of cost following which, after discussion with the director and perhaps his reference back to higher management, the requirements might need modification and a new functional specification have to be drawn up in order to secure general agreement that the overall concept is viable within an allowable cost framework.

At this stage it is of prime importance to decide on the architect/engineer arrangements. In large organisations this might be no more than contacting the architect/engineering department of the organisation which exists for work of this sort. Otherwise it will be necessary to choose an architect, preferably a firm with substantial experience in laboratory building, or failing this, if it is desirable to employ an architect without experience in the field of laboratory design, he should be requested to collaborate with a consultant with the appropriate experience.

RELATIONSHIP WITH ARCHITECT/ENGINEER

Having determined the architect/engineer arrangements the next stage will be to develop the requirements, select the site and determine the quality and character of the building. While these considerations are the responsibility of the committee, the director or even a higher authority, the advice and help of the professionals should constitute a prime element in arriving at sound conclusions.

It is likely that before the architect starts detailed work there will be some general discussions on laboratory planning and the extent to which it is possible to use modular or repetitive space units so as to cheapen construction and promote flexibility of future usage. (This should not go so far as to constrain unduly work which can only be effectively done in specialised laboratories.) The possibilities of using space which is easily inter-convertible between laboratories and offices or to have units which combine laboratory and office space also need discussion at an early stage. Pilot plant and other specialised equipment areas will often need considerable height, overhead cranage and perhaps floor wells and it may be possible to use a different modular construction for such areas.

It may be more desirable, particularly where poisonous or hazardous materials and processes are involved, to have two or more buildings, separating the administrative sectors and the less hazardous units from those of greater risk.

Apart from formalising the customer's requirements the architect must also have some understanding of how the work of the laboratory is organised. Do the senior staff expect to work in offices near to the central administration or close to, even overlooking, their laboratory areas? To what extent do junior scientists spend all their time in laboratories and not need offices at all? Is laboratory management a different function from doing research in the laboratory and what arrangements does this imply? Are the research units small or large teams, or individuals with one assistant, and should this be reflected in the size of laboratories by having unit laboratories for unit teams, or open plan laboratories for a number of teams?

The architect will also study very carefully the exceptional requirements of the customer. Thus a laboratory studying pathogenic bacteria will have very special requirements of working enclosures, directional air flows, high efficiency filtration and sterilisation arrangements which have to be treated very seriously. While it is the committee's ultimate responsibility to ensure such safety arrangements, a happy arrangement could only exist with an architect who studies such problems and gives solutions that do not require very much correction.

The general nature of the building will also need consideration in the preliminary association of committee and architect. Visits will probably be paid to existing laboratories so that different solutions to engineering and architectural problems can be examined and the faults and deficiencies of certain solutions discussed with other laboratory users. Architectural styles will also be examined, for laboratories, like other buildings, can vary from classical imitation to ultra modern: the tastes of the senior management of the parent authority would not wisely be offended in such a matter.

The future of the laboratory also needs to be considered at the formulating stage. Room for expansion should be available both within the building and for future extensions to it, but intended arrangements for changing work patterns should also be considered, not only by modular construction but by adequate space for expansion of services or even adequate central service installations to cope with future expansion. Expansion may be short term in nature and of reasonable certainty or long term and speculative, but the views of the parent organisation may have to be sought at this point since policy decisions may exist about restricting or extending the size of a given laboratory station.

Under all circumstances, the changing nature of R & D should be considered. Research departments and the projects within them grow and fade, they go from exploratory to pilot plant phases, they change substantially in nature: staff organisations also change by virtue of movement of staff, particularly of directing staff and a serious attempt should be made to slow down the obsolescence which potentially arises from this changing pattern in the laboratory building.

When these preliminaries of general laboratory pattern, nature of laboratory units, special features, nature of building and attitude towards expansion and flexibility have been clarified, the next stage will be to aim at the architect's rough cost estimate. Such an estimate should be within something like + 20 per cent and should carry a contingency of about 10 per cent. Working at this level designs do not have to be decided in detail, but it is necessary that nearly every requirement of the laboratory is included. For this purpose the architect will submit his own questionnaire to the customer. It will, of course, be on similar lines to the functional specification previously shown, but in greater depth and detail.

As a result of this estimate further adjustment to the overall design may become necessary, some features may be removed, the quality of finish may be lessened, areas of working space available may be lessened so that the total cost comes nearer to the level of finance available: or a pause may be necessary while the higher cost goes through an authorising procedure.

However, the stage then arises where approval in principle is obtained and the design has to be decided on in detail, architectural and engineering drawings are produced in sufficient detail for accurate estimating, and the architect has to keep the customer closely informed of how the design is developing.

It is very important that departures from the preliminary design should not occur either on the part of the architect or the customer without full mutual understanding of the technical effect on the one side and the cost effect on the other. This can only be done by close working between the architect and the customer committee. Neither the architect nor customer must be free to change the design without the other's knowledge. The design, however, will be going through a crucial stage when important matters of detail and of substance can easily be omitted if the customer does not have close contact and understanding of the drawings and specifications produced.

A construction cost estimate should now be arrived at which should be very close to the more reasonable of those actually bid and the customer will be invited to accept the design, and after any final modifications, the architect can proceed with working drawings, the placing of main building contracts and whatever sub-contracting is required in accordance with one of the standard building contract procedures, in agreement with the customer.

After the building contract has been awarded it is highly desirable that no further changes should be made to the design for not only will the cost go up more than proportionally but because of the ramifications on other design aspects, new mistakes can easily creep in while the 'desirable' modification is being made. On the other hand it is inevitable that the scientists will require modifications which they will think essential. It requires a very firm hand on the part of the chairman of the guiding committee, with perhaps a rule to the effect that modifications can only be allowed after the cost and time effects have been calculated and with the personal approval of someone at directing level.

In this way the design of the laboratory should be in accordance with the wishes of the research director and his staff and meet the approval of the parent authority. A satisfactory relationship with the architect should obtain with adequate control of detailed design on the one side and of cost on the other. Modifications subsequent to the 'freezing' of a design should be few and carefully controlled.

SELECTION OF SITE

Many elements are involved in the selection of a satisfactory site for a new laboratory. There may well be completely overriding considerations – the new laboratory may be intended as an extension to an existing laboratory complex or as a service to an existing industrial undertaking at a centralised site. Otherwise the considerations will be the usual ones for technical undertakings, such as the existence of adequate basic utilities – water, electricity, gas, storm and sanitary sewers, roads, transport connections for air and rail traffic –, suitable soil conditions for foundations and drainage, and space for future expansion.

There will, moreover, be special considerations for a laboratory since, as we have seen, the most important factor in the laboratory is to attract and hold suitably highly qualified staff. Better than average working conditions are, therefore, desirable, with pleasant buildings well spaced and well landscaped, avoidance of industrial areas but with ample facilities for living, eating, banking and shopping within reasonably short distances from the laboratory, which should not be remote from easy communication with good centres of civilisation. Failure to achieve these criteria, though not prohibitive, will nevertheless inevitably produce penalties in administration and management.

CONTROL OF BUILDING ACTIVITIES

Once the building contract has been let, it would usually be the architect's preference that it be proceeded with uninterruptedly, with the customer having no more to do with it until it is completed. Unfortunately, for a modern laboratory – particularly where special new features are incorporated such as windtunnels, radioactive areas or model ship testing tanks – the dialogue between scientist and architect in arriving at a design is not perfect; the scientist frequently does not find it easy to understand the detail drawings produced, and the architect or his engineer does not easily understand the more sophisticated concepts he is asked to engineer.

It can be a considerable help to use other methods to assist in this dialogue before the building is proceeded with, such as

(a) Building a three-dimensional model of the 'working' parts of the laboratory. This can be an extremely useful method, at only small cost relative to the building cost, of visualising to the scientist the nature of the engineering concept of his ideas, and of helping the architect in discussing problems of construction and planning other aspects of the building. It is also extremely useful later in the life of the building for training scientists and operating staff and explaining the laboratory to visitors.

(b) Building full scale 'mock-ups' of particularly intricate sections of the laboratory facilities – even of typical service run method. This enables the scientist to make small alterations for convenience purposes (e.g. where do the gloves most conveniently go in a glove box having an intricate machine or where do the machine controls go so as to be easily operated) and to confirm the overall design. This should, of course, be done before the design is finalised.

(c) Where off-site, sub-contracted manufacture is used and where the critical path network allows, it is sometimes possible to pre-erect complete units or part units at the subcontractors' works or on site, for inspection and even testing before disassembly and re-erection in its proper place. This, carried out under observation of the scientist concerned, can eliminate the necessity of modification later and therefore cheapen modifications, particularly if the unit tested is one of many, and equally in the latter case it can save on time and cost in the overall construction.

With or without these aids to the satisfactory building of a laboratory, it is still desirable from the scientist's point of view that he should be a close observer of the actual building construction and be represented at site construction meetings. What should be clear, however, is that only the architect is empowered to instruct the main builder or sub-contractors, and the scientist can only instruct the architect through some formalised arrangement as mentioned above. A loss in construction time and escalation in cost inevitably attend the situation where scientists are free to ask the builder to include any modifications he wishes.

COMMISSIONING AND TAKE-OVER

When the laboratory construction is finished, the very important function of bringing it into commission and eventually handing it over to the customer has to take place.

It is important to distinguish between the commissioning that is the responsibility of the architect and that which is the responsibility of the customer, at least so far as specialised laboratory equipment is concerned. The dividing line will depend on how the specification has been worded, but it is usual for the architect to be responsible for achieving certain physical conditions – temperature, humidity, air speeds, electrical parameters, volume throughputs of gases, gas purities – for a given section of the laboratory or piece of equipment, but whether when those parameters are reached the equipment will perform the scientific function expected of it would normally be the responsibility of the customer.

The following phases therefore appear in the take-over procedure

(a) *'Mechanical/electrical' commissioning*   This would be the responsibility of the architect who would probably set up commissioning teams consisting of his own staff, the builders' staff and customer observers. The function of these teams would be to set up schedules of testing and inspection for the different sections of the laboratory and its equipment, with the object of satisfying themselves that specifications had been met in all particulars. The customer observers who might represent both the eventual building operators and the scientists who are to work with the equipment would be present to satisfy themselves that such a schedule of tests and inspection was adequate. These commissioning teams would also devise satisfactory tests and assemble test gear and eventually, when the building section concerned was reported complete, would arrange for the tests and inspection to be carried out.

(b) *Modification* It is most unlikely that the testing and inspection stages will fail to divulge some inadequacy in the building. The special equipment may not come quite up to expectation, and some parts of the building and its equipment will be found to be incomplete or not finished to the required standard. Sometimes there will be a considerable effort required to adjust equipment so that it does reach specification, or perhaps some modification will be required or error corrected before it does. Items not finished satisfactorily will have to be redone and altogether a reasonable period of time must be allowed for this modification stage.

(c) *Re-testing* When the modifications are said to be complete retesting of the appropriate parts of the building will take place. It is likely that at this stage the building will be acceptable to the customer, perhaps with a statement of reservation. The customer is then able to take over the building with the reservations being attended to by the architect or builder in accordance with some prearranged formula.

(d) The customer organisation will now carry out its own functional commissioning activities to establish that the equipment, while satisfactory in its mechanical and physical parameters, will also carry out the processes for which it was intended. It may well be that further modifications will be sought at this time either because of scientific progress which has occurred since the equipment was first specified or because, in spite of the best efforts at close specification, the processes are not being effectively carried out. Such modifications, however, are entirely outside the terms of the architect's contract and have to be approved and financed in some separate fashion.

The many phases involved in building a new laboratory will be seen to be intricate and time consuming. Few modern laboratories can be left for an architect to assemble a number of standard units, thread them with standard services and house them into a pleasing shell. In nearly all cases research involves large, special, and costly equipment as the main hub of the laboratory, to be designed and housed in a careful fashion, with a multiplicity of specialist sub-contractors, as well as the laboratories' scientists, intimately involved and with a large array of piped services, many of which have to be generated on the site. The scientists must be closely concerned with all those phases from initial concept to completion of the building and the management ultimately responsible for the building has to plan its forces and its contribution to the building in a careful way with much knowledge of the problems that can arise.

A laboratory building is successful if the functions expected of it can be carried out smoothly and efficiently not only when it is first built but through successive changes in work pattern which may reasonably be expected to emerge in the future.

LABORATORY MANAGEMENT

The efficient running of laboratories has become in recent years an issue of great concern in that laboratories become more complicated and house complex equipment of many hazards at a time when technicians and labour skilled in equipment operation get more scarce. [77]

Administratively, a problem arises concerning the responsibilities of the scientists who are in the laboratory to perform research and not to look after the many routine concerns of the laboratory, as compared with laboratory management responsibilities.

It is neither possible nor desirable to absolve the scientist entirely from considerations of the safety of the operations which only he knows expertly or from the supply of special materials for his experimental work. On the other hand he does not usually wish to concern himself with framing regulations, arranging supplies and the like.

Also a scientist is likely, even at a senior level, not to wish to concern himself with the management of laboratory staff or even the routine operation of experimental rigs for the research itself.

It is surprising that in many large laboratories the problem is not taken as seriously as it deserves, and each section is frequently left to work out its laboratory management arrangements as best it can, with scientists, laboratory technicians and senior foremen of laboratory operations settling into some pattern mutually convenient to the personalities concerned.

It is strongly advisable, however, that a firm appointment of laboratory manager should be made for any large laboratory or group of laboratories in which a number of separate scientific sections work.

Among his duties might be

(a) To manage the laboratory labour and technician forces, planning their work in accordance with the demands of various scientists, looking after personnel matters, such as work study application and labour training in liaison with the personnel department, and be concerned with local disciplinary and supervision duties.

(b) To be concerned with the operation of general services in the laboratory such as demineralisation, low temperature, special gas production, gas cylinders, laboratory furniture requirements, and to be responsible, under the direction of the appropriate scientist, for the erection and operation of experimental rigs, and equipment such as ovens, balances, darkrooms.

(c) The management of stores in the laboratory – probably in liaison with a central stores organisation – being concerned with arranging the particular specialist stores of the laboratory and accountability and protection of them when they are particularly dangerous and/or expensive; looking after the economy of stores usage and maximising the use of special instruments. Looking after the necessary paperwork local to the laboratory for receipts and despatch.

(d) Responsibility for the preparation and storage of reagents (chemical and biological), fixatives, stains, indicators and any other special reagents or standard materials such as solvents in general or permanent use in the laboratory.

(e) Responsibility for the periodic inspection of laboratories and their workshops and the routine overhaul and maintenance both in respect of items for which there are statutory requirements, such as pressure vessels and lifting equipment, and other specialised equipment. Looking after routine maintenance schedules and schedules for return of equipment for inspection such as electrical equipment. Seeing to the cleaning of laboratories with their apparatus, equipment and furniture and generally to be responsible for good housekeeping in the laboratory.

(f) To be responsible for the care of the laboratories from a safety point of view. Ensuring that imposed regulations are applied and local regulations drawn up in relation to fire hazards and special hazards of the laboratory, poisons, explosives, inflammability, disposal of chemicals, electrical dangers, radiation, biological hazards and workshop dangers. Ensuring that satisfactory procedures are available for first aid or for communication with the central medical facilities. The Factories Acts and their implications to the particular laboratories should be understood and administered.

(g) The maintenance of laboratory records and technical information systems – filing control, arranging disposal of old material, keeping relevant trade catalogues, films, and operating copying machinery.

(h) Because the maintenance of satisfactory relations with outside organisations is essential to any successful laboratory and therefore it is likely visitors will be frequent, it is advisable to place the staging of exhibitions on a planned basis, rather than try to formulate a new plan for each visit. The laboratory manager should be responsible for the maintenance of a permanent exhibition in the laboratory, in consultation with scientists and engineers which will give a succinct picture of the important work of the laboratories. This needs to be continually updated. The laboratory manager will also be much concerned with planning for open days with more elaborate displays and with arranging displays for external events such as trade shows, etc.

All these duties have to be performed in any laboratory from the smallest upwards, and where the laboratory is of any size they should not be left to chance or divided haphazardly between the scientists in the laboratory. On the other hand the terms of reference of the laboratory manager should do nothing to alleviate the responsibility of each scientist in respect of his own experimentation for sound design, operation, safety and maintenance.

Unfortunately there does not appear to be any recognised training ground or even qualification for a fully taught and experienced manager and these duties have a tendency therefore gradually to fall to the ablest of the senior technicians or senior foreman. There is a decided requirement for greater recognition of a laboratory manager career.

SUMMARY

Most scientists at managing level will at some time be involved in planning new laboratory accommodation. The methods of procedure to obtain what is wanted by the scientists in the best architectural/engineering form are considered.

It is a good idea to set up a planning working party with appropriate membership. A first functional specification will then be produced in answer to the listed questionnaire and the architect/engineer arrangements have then to be considered. After preliminary discussions, the architect/engineer will produce a preliminary design and costing which after successive adjustments will form the basis for contracting. Departures from design after that point should only be allowed through some formal arrangement which considers the technical and cost impacts.

Once the building contract has been let its control has to be considered with the scientists' representative assisting in a continuous dialogue with the contractor. Useful aids are the building of models, the building of a full scale mock-up of difficult sections and sometimes the pre-erection at contractor's site of complete units.

Commissioning of buildings and their equipment is done in two stages:

(a) Electro/mechanical commissioning to ensure that the contractor has achieved the physical parameters laid down.
(b) Functional commissioning by the scientist organisation to make sure that the equipment carries out the processes intended.

The many phases involved in building a new laboratory are intricate and time consuming and a laboratory building is successful only if the functions expected of it can be carried out smoothly and efficiently through successive changes in work pattern which can be anticipated.

Laboratory management is a function which is all too often left largely to chance without there being any adequate recognised qualification and career structure.

A correct relationship between laboratory management and working scientists which does not absolve the latter from interest in and responsibility for safety and efficient operation but which relieves them of time wasting on various laboratory administration problems is desirable.

A laboratory manager's duties would involve responsibilities in connection with

(a) Management of technician and labour forces

(b) Operation of general services

(c) Management of local stores

(d) Preparation and management of reagents, solvents and other standard materials

(e) Periodic inspection of laboratories for good housekeeping

(f) Safety, both special and general

(g) Mounting of exhibitions, etc.

10 Technical assistance to R & D staff

SERVICES-DIRECT AND INDIRECT

In a research establishment there are specialist activities providing a service to the establishment and what they are and what they do can seriously affect the research activity itself.

They can be divided into those services directly related to the research activity like engineering, information services, contracts and safety advisers, and indirect services such as the payment of wages, estate management, transport, and medical services. The line of demarcation between the two is not clear cut. Thus the accounts department can be a service to the research activity in providing funds and providing a central mechanism for purchasing, but it can be indirect in so far as it is related to expenditure outside the research activity and in so far as it relates to satisfying the financial requirements of the parent organisation.

The organisation of such services presents a complicated issue. It is normally dealt with in large government research establishments by having an engineering department which supplies design, engineering manufacture, maintenance of buildings, equipment and civil installations and the operation of services like steam, refrigeration, effluent, etc., while all other 'non-engineering' services are operated by the administrative division.

The danger inherent in this simple organisation is that, particularly in large organisations, these departments grow into self-sufficiency, organise themselves for their own convenience and efficiency, and succeed to a lesser extent in operating for the needs of the research activity.

Such considerations are leading to closer attention being

given in some cases to separating the 'direct' services from the 'indirect', with the management of the direct services being answerable to the same senior direction as the R & D activity. In this way a greater assurance is thought to obtain that operation of such direct services will be related to the needs of the R & D activities.

INFORMATION AND LIBRARY SERVICES

The information and library service is among the most important of the R & D services and it can affect the efficiency of conduct of research to a very marked, though subtle and largely hidden extent. The researcher requires the books, reports and other information that he knows about in a rapid service, he wants to keep them for as long as is necessary to be useful to his work, and he wants to be reminded to return them to the library in due course. But he also wants an information service to bring to his attention the literature on his subject that he is not aware of. It is, therefore, not unusual for information officers to perform an abstracting service, disseminating their abstracts to appropriate research workers. The library would also deal with the purchase, display and circulation of appropriate learned journals, and the researcher wants the right journals to be obtained and the more important ones circulated to him at an early date after their publication.

In all these three activities a very lively and effective communication system between the information service and the working scientists is essential for efficient and useful operation.

Books on the shelves which are not even remotely relevant to the work of the establishment, to the exclusion of modern books which are, reports coming in which relate to project areas long finished by the establishment, information abstracts going out to workers who no longer work in that field, the arrival of circulated journals many months out of date are the real signs of an inadequate information service which any amount of computer retrieval systems and modern classifications cannot hide from the working scientists, though they appeal to the senior management who control the information service as signs of efficient operation. The communication between information services and scientists, therefore, must be fostered so that scientists assist in the selection of books, notify information services of changes in information requirements and maintain a lively interchange regarding the use of periodicals. A happy working relationship between researcher and information officer can be mutually fruitful – the researcher will save an immense amount of time by not repeating work which has already been described in the literature, the information officer will be motivated by appreciation of the creative value of his work. He should be active and aggressive in associating himself with 'customer' needs.

The information services are likely to be also responsible for the editing and reproduction of reports, involving such problems as looking after commercial security and higher policy in connection with publication, and may well encompass such things as looking after patent activities, licensing activities, etc.

In these activities, information officers, patent officers and the like are in a special position in having a wide knowledge of the activities going on in the establishment, looking at them from a balanced point of view and also are closely in touch with much that is involved in higher policy activities. They should, therefore, be in a good position themselves to produce the literature that emanates from research laboratories as brochures, exhibition literature, publicity handouts and the like, which scientists usually find frustrating to have to do, and it may well be useful for them to be the writers of technical documentation concerning the contractor–customer relations of the establishment, producing technical programmes, periodical reports of contract activity, technical specifications and other writing, leaving the scientists to produce research or project technical reports as they progress.

This is an extension of what is normally asked of the information department and it could only be achieved if the right proportion of the funds of the research establishment were subscribed to it. There is usually, however, a tendency to reduce the expenditure on information services while expecting ever-expanding services from it.

ENGINEERING SERVICES

A very considerable contribution is made to research and development by engineering development, such as design and manufacture of experimental equipment, planning and installation in connection with new laboratory facilities, the manufacture of prototypes and other 'ironmongery' connected with research, the maintenance of buildings and services such as steam, electricity, refigeration, effluent, and the operation of special services. We have considered in Chapter 3 the special problems involved in engineering design as related to research in project development, in Chapter 7 we have considered how engineering services might be organised to improve the efficiency of research activities.

No modern, sophisticated engineering services effort can be effectively organised without all these factors and others being taken into account. No single system can be conceived of as correct in all circumstances and it is certainly the job of a scientific management to try to ensure that the best organisation is available for a given research activity.

A typical organisation might be one where all service engineers came under a central engineering division but with a personalised service on loan to certain research groups – this might consist of simply a liaison engineer or a group of design engineers with their own machine shop facilities –, some small machine shop service available for direct service, but with the main large-scale engineering operations on a centralised basis.

ADMINISTRATIVE CONTROLS

The necessity of administrative controls, like the necessity of budgeting, cannot be avoided in an R & D department, although there is a basic conflict which can never be resolved satisfactorily between the necessity of as much freedom as possible in carrying out scientific work, as against the necessity of providing a smooth controlled machinery of administration. On the one hand complete freedom is never obtainable, on the other, administrative controls should never exist for the convenience of the administrator. The larger and more complex the laboratory the more difficult does the problem become, because behaviour patterns have to be codified and then interpreted in the light of data available only to the administrator, whereas in a small laboratory the director can institute controls more easily understandable to his scientists which more closely relate to the real needs of the laboratory.

In a large laboratory there are problems like centralisation of services – typing, general administration, transport – versus decentralisation to scientific divisions, central purchasing with formal tendering procedures, priorities in demands on services, timekeeping and its control. The latter is a practically insoluble problem because it can never be seriously argued that the productivity of a professional scientist or engineer is dependent on keeping to set hours, but since the laboratory will have larger numbers of hourly paid workers conditioned to strict time keeping, and who nevertheless will in some cases be paid more and be more valuable than junior scientists, it is desirable that scientists shall not appear to have a more relaxed environment. In a small laboratory none of these problems becomes important so long as the director and his managers are reasonably understanding of the motivation of the different groups.

Each laboratory is, therefore, likely to tackle its administrative problems in a different fashion and guiding principles only can be given. The first is the necessity for continual critical appraisal by research management and administrators of administrative controls dictated to the research division by external authority. Secondly, it is no less necessary to exercise continuous self criticism of administrative arrangements initiated within the research establishment or division. The criticism should be towards examining whether the control is necessary for the efficient working of the research teams and not simply to solve an administrative problem in the easiest way for the administrator. Thirdly, the communication of controls from administrators to the staff needs careful consideration. It is necessary to avoid the image of control administrators issuing streams of instructions which appear to cripple the working of the scientists. Mechanisms for subjecting draft instructions to scientific scrutiny and for securing changes to existing procedures should not only exist but be known to exist even by junior scientists. The reasons for issuing instructions should be given wherever possible.

The elimination of all conflict between administrators and scientists is not likely to be achieved, but determined efforts in that direction are worth making in order to relieve the frustrations of both the working scientists and the working administrator and to foster the idea of partnership between them.

It has been argued that a scientific establishment gets the administrators it deserves and that behind every successful laboratory is an efficient administrative machine.

SAFETY

It is almost in the nature of research and development work, not only that it presents potential hazards, but that these are continually changing. Safety, therefore, plays a very important part in laboratory operations and its organisation is a matter deserving careful attention. Perhaps a first principle is that there should be someone who has a special responsibility for safety, in the exercise of which he is responsible only to the head of the establishment. In a small laboratory this may only be a part-time post: in a large laboratory the safety officer might well be the director of a substantial division. It would be the duty of the safety department to be aware of the hazards involved in all the activities of the laboratory, to accumulate and disseminate knowledge concerning them – carrying out research themselves if necessary – and to issue instructions of a general nature which apply over a wide field of operations.

It is, however, equally a sound principle that everybody should be considered as being responsible for his own safety and for the safety of those working for him. It would follow that it is everybody's duty to acquaint the safety department with new operations that might involve hazard and to liaise with them to obtain enough information to enable them to issue the appropriate instructions to their staff and operate their experiments suitably. This principle is sound because if the safety department is considered 'responsible' for safety – a concept of doubtful validity anyway – there will be an inclination for other workers to leave it to them and to blame them if accidents occur.

The two principles are not inconsistent if it is considered that the function of the safety department is to be advisory to all others. They can advise directly from the knowledge they have or by going into a laboratory noting that something needs doing, or indirectly by waiting for the approach of the other department to request advice.

In the direct case one can either have a positive system of regular (or irregular) inspection of laboratories and work places at the instance of the safety department or the less positive one of inspection on invitation (again regularly or irregularly). The advantage of the positive inspection system is that unsatisfactory practices by staff who are not very safety conscious are more likely to be unearthed. Its disadvantage is that the desirable spirit of co-operation between safety expert and scientist is less likely to be fostered if it is felt that 'snooping' is occurring and also that again there would be a greater tendency to leave safety to the safety department.

A useful compromise approach is for the divisional director to issue a standard invitation for the safety department to review the activities in his division on some regular basis and to make it known to the staff that this is the basis of the safety department's visits.

We have been concerned in the above mainly with those hazards which relate to the research activity. In addition, in all laboratories there will be more common hazards associated with statutory regulations such as relate to pressure vessels, lifting gear and various Factories Acts requirements, and the use of equipment for 'mechanical safety' such as goggles, special boots, respirators, etc. The supply, testing, insurance arrangements, etc., associated with these aspects of safety is best removed from the responsibility of the research worker and dealt with by the safety or engineering service departments as appropriate on a centralised basis.

Having set up the general organisation for dealing with safety, it remains a continuing and taxing problem to ensure that safety is continually kept a live issue without presenting considerable impediment to prosecution of the research work, particularly in large research establishments where the central safety department can be remote from individual laboratories. Useful devices for maintaining the necessary inputs include (a) occasional direct discussion between the management of the research division and safety staff, (b) the setting up of safety committees in groups of laboratories to examine the implication of new regulations and to consider the new hazards that might arise in those laboratories, (c) the maintaining of special exercises such as fire evacuation of buildings which both encourage familiarity with required methods and increase awareness of safety matters, (d) the framing of regulations relating to the operation of plant or equipment with special hazards and (e) appointing safety liaison officers in each laboratory to take a special interest in the safety of the laboratory, (f) the drawing up of codes of practice relative to the work of the laboratory. It is also important within a laboratory hierarchy that safety and health responsibilities should be clearly defined for each level of hierarchy with written statements pinpointing the appropriate devolution of responsibilities.[78]

The job of the director is to ensure that an organisation exists for dealing with all safety matters, for bringing to the attention of the appropriate level of staff not only accidents but incidents which might have given rise to accidents, and for maintaining communications between the safety organisation and the laboratories and within laboratories.

CONSULTANTS

It will have been clear from much of this book that an important message in the effective use of research and development is not to do it unless it is necessary for the attainment of the objective because the knowledge required cannot be obtained elsewhere sufficiently cheaply.

Very useful technical assistance to a research department can be given by the use of consultants, if carefully chosen because the knowledge they have is in a field which bears directly on some of the research work in the laboratory. Hopefully they may eliminate the need for some projected research programme because they already have the knowledge or because they can suggest a more economic research approach, but more likely they might be expected to reduce it by suggesting good techniques, areas where published work is relevant and finally help in interpreting results to give more and better information.

The research manager will, therefore, encourage the use of consultants who can be of such help (and discourage those who merely waste the time of the research scientists) and will himself endeavour to maintain contacts to help to establish the best consultant service.

Equally the special knowledge that any research establishment has can be used to establish a consultancy service to other organisations. Care has to be exercised that in this way information which could be the basis of effective licensing agreements is not sold too cheaply. On the other hand it should be used to help exploit licensable situations. Providing a consultancy service should help to establish the reputation of a laboratory, provide some income, cause a wider dissemination of scientific knowledge and provide profit opportunities for the laboratory.

HUMAN SCIENCES

The use of physical or biological science is so common in industrial and other technologically-based operations such as defence and health that its absence would cause more surprise than its presence in any large undertaking. The opposite, however, remains true of the use of human or social scientists, although the problems of maximising work output, reducing strain and friction on and between operations at all levels, promoting job enrichment, providing the right incentives, developing human potential, are problems to which social scientists increasingly address themselves and can have appreciable effect, particularly in rapidly changing science-based environments.

It is not because the systematic study of human factors in industry is new. It was put on an official footing in the 'Health of Munitions Workers' Committee' during the First World War; the classical Hawthorne studies in the USA were conducted over thirty years ago and the work of social scientists in the army and in certain large industries has established many principles of human behaviour which can be applied to industrial-type operations. Indeed there are many current concepts in the staff management problems of organisations which have been developed in recent years by psychologists, sociologists and management thinkers. They have developed from the scientific study and prediction of human behaviour in a social setting, and a growing body of knowledge exists upon which management, particularly personnel management, can draw. Some of this work, where it particularly appertains to the research station has been discussed in other chapters.

Among the studies which have such relevance are

(a) physical capacity such as sight, hearing, touch, task muscular strength, interpreting, decision making in relation to machinery or industrial processes.

(b) the selection of the right people for the right job – whether on a manual or management plane.

(c) the relationship of external physical conditions with output.

(d) analysis of operational requirements in relation to training – again whether manual, management or even for scientific research itself.

(e) ergonomics.

(f) effective working of groups (work groups or committees), particularly in changing work patterns.

(g) effectiveness of organisations and their life cycles. (Patterns of organisations appear to be common to successful enterprises but they change with changing stages of technological life.)

(h) response of organisations to rapid change conditioned by external forces.

(i) mechanistic v. organic command structures for different types of organised activity.

The first problem of the human sciences, however, is to command much more widespread acceptance. That this will now develop more quickly is to be expected from the recent formation of the Social Science Research Council, the setting up at the Warren Spring Laboratory of the Department of Trade and Industry of a human sciences section, and the greatly increased interests of students in opting for the social sciences which will provide a larger body of expertise to apply to the appropriate problems. Government spending on the social sciences increased from £2,281,000 in 1966/67 to £7,200,000 in 1970/71.

It is perhaps not an unreal expectation that eventually nearly every sizeable laboratory concerned with serving a major enterprise will have a human sciences section to study the activities of the enterprise and to act as advisers to management based on knowledge of up-to-date behavioural science.

The establishment and functioning of technical services of direct impingement on research activities will thus be seen to be of considerable importance in enabling the research worker to operate with the best assistance and under circumstances which reduce frustration to an acceptable level. These activities therefore always deserve the careful attention of research management.

SUMMARY

In any research establishment there are a number of specialist services which either provide direct assistance to the scientist such as engineering, information services, contracts and safety advisers, or an indirect service such as payment of wages, many personnel problems, estate management, security, transport.

There is a case for separating these two so that those of a direct nature are answerable to the same senior direction as the R & D activity.

Information and library services have a more positive part to play than merely providing books and disseminating periodicals and reports. It is desirable to foster a positive relationship between information officers and scientists so that the information needs of the latter, both incoming and outgoing, can be intelligently and rapidly met.

Engineering services have a difficult duty and it is important to organise the right relationship so that scientist get some direct assistance in the day-to-day running of their laboratories and a more elaborate service for their wider and more costly needs, keeping those of the profession of engineering under some sort of control 'umbrella'.

The necessity of administrative controls of various sorts cannot be avoided although they are often regarded with hostility by scientists. The fostering of good working relationships with a continued criticism of the ultimate necessity of each administrative control and their careful introduction is desirable.

Continually changing potential hazards are nearly always associated with scientific research and the organisation to ensure continual awareness of such hazards and how best to deal with them are important, particularly in the relationships between central safety specialists and laboratory operators. Safety responsibilities should always be clearly defined.

The case for greater involvement of the human sciences in all the organisational concerns of research and development is argued as being a development that is overdue but likely to arise substantially in the near future.

11 Leadership in research organisations

We have seen that there are a number of management techniques that have been modified to form new and useful tools to help in the operation of a Research and Development establishment: that there are considerations of relationship of research to objectives and of successful research practice which have produced their own problems and their own methods of organisation: that there are problems in increasing the efficiency of conducting research itself which increases the output in relation to reaching objectives for a given expenditure.

We have at the same time sought throughout the book to make it clear that directing good research can never be done simply by the use of management tools alone. This can only be achieved by forming the environment that the individual research worker requires to be creative and active, and then fusing the activities of individual workers into a whole which is greater than the sum of individual parts, both in producing scientific advance and in achieving project objectives.

ANALOGY WITH ORCHESTRAL PLAYING

The process of co-operative research may be likened to orchestral playing with the director as the conductor, the research managers as the section leaders and the individual research workers as players. The team will be built up in accordance with what 'music' you want to play – and good musicians will only be happy to play good music. The repertory will be chosen for many reasons – suitability to the orchestra, suitability to the customer, even, since the commercial viability of the orchestra is essential, i.e. what will pay adequately. The conductor then has to balance the orchestra so that it produces the right sounds, make sure it plays to the right time schedule and finally he must draw from it something creative that transcends the sum of its individual players. The conductor may conceivably be a better violinist than any in the orchestra but he will leave violin playing to the violinist. The violinist might be a better violinist than the conductor is a conductor, but he does not conduct the orchestra.

Similarly, the research director must draw his creative contribution from balancing his team, getting them to work together and aiming for a creative objective which transcends the mere addition of individual workers' contributions, each of which might nevertheless be a greater act of creation than the director himself performs.

Just as the conductor can only perform with a lot of technical knowledge, however, so can the director. Written music is itself a sort of critical path network in which the musical events are allotted time elements, the resources of the orchestra are indicated and phased together to reach the musical objective of the composer. The conductor sees that the network achieves its objectives, making small changes as he goes along, a difference being perhaps that in research the director and his staff are writing the 'music' as well as playing it.

Orchestras work better if their finances are sound, the players are picked carefully and subjected to careful training in the formative years (particularly in orchestral playing), if there is an efficient ordering of their ancillary services, their libraries are in good order and the halls in which they play have been carefully designed.

No doubt, like most broad analogies this could be faulted in many particulars but the main intention is to convey the sense in which the creativity of both research and the management of research are at the same time greater than the discipline of management tools but all the better for their use.

PLACE OF INDIVIDUAL RESEARCH WORKER

The relationship of the individual research worker to the directing level is one in which, also, care must be taken to remove the concept of manager and managed as far as possible. The research worker is doing a creative job in his own right and this work is in no sense being 'managed' from above. On the other hand, adjusting a research worker's programme to fit into the overal plan is a necessary activity of the research management chain. Also, if the director happens to have a special expertise in a particular section of work, he may well be able to make suggestions on the conduct of the work itself. He would do well not to demand that they be accepted.

These comments are valid in relation to highly academic research, where overall objectives should exist, as much as to objective-orientated research in industry or elsewhere.

MAINTAINING HIGH STANDARDS

If good research work and well integrated projects are to come out of a research establishment it is necessary to pay continuous attention to maintaining the highest standards that the staff are capable of. In research, the average worker can be spurred to attainments beyond his expectations or decline into routine work, and the former must be a continuous objective of the director. Perhaps of first importance is to place the research worker in association with others whose abilities are better than his own by virtue of natural ability or sound experience, at the same time ensuring that the group are temperamentally congenial. The worker should also form part of a team, the leader of which sets a standard to be aimed at. Secondly the research managers and, if necessary, the director will refuse to accept reports which are not of a good scientific standard describing sound work: for then a worker will not obtain the satisfaction of 'published' work unless he has earned it and will adjust his sights accordingly. (By publication may only be meant limited circulation within the research department.) Thirdly workers should, if they demonstrate potential, have the opportunity to participate at higher level discussions and conferences so that they can observe the strategic situation into which their work fits and so challenge themselves into making their work stand up to a higher standard.

It is in the practice of developing staff by such means that another element of creativity comes into the director's work.

The carrying out of research itself and directing it so that it achieves unity is still not a sufficient, although it is a necessary target. Even in purely academic research the integrated work of a department will be all the more useful if it fits into and augments other academic activities in related fields. In project-orientated work it is even more essential that the total research effort of a department interplays with other research effort on the project and with design and customer requirements. Much has been written of this interplay in this book. It is mentioned here as another aspect of the creative element in research direction.

LEADERSHIP

The problems of leadership have been given attention as a sociological study in recent years. It may be seen as a special sort of power with a wide range of behaviours and, as touched on in Chapter 8, it is related to the charismatic or referent type of power – power conceded by force of personality although it is clearly also an example of legitimate power of great strength. It involves in Etzioni's words '. . . the ability based on the personal qualities of the leader, to elicit the followers voluntary compliance in a broad range of matters. Leadership is distinguished from the concept of power in that it entails influence, i.e. the change of preferences, while power only implies that the subjects' preferences are held in abeyance.' [79]

The director of research, in leading creative work, has particularly the need for such a concept of leadership.

Critical tasks of high level leadership fall into four categories:

(a) definition of organisational role – this is a dynamic process, for as we have seen the organisational role is varied by internal and external pressure, but it is necessary to have as clear and singular a goal as possible;
(b) creating the institutional embodiment of purpose – deciding upon the means in terms of resources, policy and organisational structure, to achieve the aims desired;

(c) defending the organisation's integrity – both internally by building up a consistent identity which has a self integrity, and by presenting to the external environment an image of what the organisation stands for;

(d) the ordering of internal conflict – the resolution of problems in terms of reforming the organisation's competence to meet its aims. [80]

In these concepts the director has the special dual function of seeing that his establishment or department is functioning efficiently in an instrumental or task-orientated fashion and providing the socio-emotional requirements for establishing internal morale and external acceptance. More than simply giving orders and making decisions and acting on them, it is the persuasion of individuals towards inventive ideas, and arriving at consensus decisions, that differentiate leadership from sheer possession of power. Equally, in relationship with 'client' organisations, he needs the ability not merely to accept orders, but to present the capabilities of his organisation and influence the client when he is arriving at his decisions.

Different situations demand different forms of leadership, and therefore different leaders, because different skills and behaviours will be called for in each different situation. Sometimes the tasks of the organisation can be carried out efficiently but the aims of the organisation are not clear or the relationship with a new environment needs to be built up afresh. Carefully sorting out the needs of the organisation in the terms given here should help in arriving at a decision as to which type of leader is to be looked for.

LEADERSHIP STYLES

From what has already been said it will be seen that leadership can be focused around two contrasting styles of leadership role. These are the authoritarian (task) and supportive (socio-emotional) approaches. ·

The authoritarian is likely to be characterised by a leader of great personal ability, who knows what is wanted to achieve the tasks of the organisation and can issue instructions accordingly, but who is more likely to do so by the use of power and 'punishment'.

Such an approach may well be more effective in stable, structured situations where a goal has to be reached on a given, short, time scale; and where information required for decision-making is clear and where decisions have to be made rapidly. In fact, development projects in which the elements of research can be clearly spelled out may well come within such a category.

The supportive style is likely to be characterised by the leader showing greater consideration for his employees, by using consultative machinery for decision-making and by exercising only general supervision with mostly delegated authority. It is also to be preferred where the subordinates are of a type who just want to get on with their jobs and do not wish to participate in management.

This style would probably be best where decisions are difficult and require considerable feedback of information for them to be effective, where there is time for decisions to come to fruition and where subordinates have an inclination to help in the decision-making process. It is probably also to be preferred in a situation of change, external threat or ambiguity of goals. [81]

In practice, and particularly is this so with research organisations, neither of these two styles is likely to be adopted in a pure form. The two will be mixed and one will predominate over the other only to a limited degree.

Clearly, as in most other aspects of complex organisations such as one finds in large R & D departments, the problem of leadership is itself a complex one. It is perhaps unfortunate that research departments tend to be particularly dynamic in the way of changing goals, changing relations with their technological environment, and changing situation in the life of their major projects – with the life of individual leaders being longer than the periods of stability in any one form.

TYPICAL RESPONSIBILITIES OF HEAD OF R & D DEPARTMENT

While the problem of leadership in its general sense is the most important for the head of research activities, as for other activities involving staff activation, the technical nature of the job is also of importance and requires to be understood. The following elements are proposed as those that are likely to figure in a description of the activities of such an R & D head. [26]

The responsibility of the R & D department will be the discovery of new scientific and engineering principles in technical areas of current or potential interest to the parent authority, with a second and equally important responsibility to build enough utility into the principles discovered so that application possibilities can be realised. Allied to this is the promotion of those new principles to whoever are potential users. Aside from good contacts in the parent authority the department will have extensive, close relations with university departments, working agreements with outside organisations and responsible contact with present and prospective 'users' of the know-how evolved.

The skills required go well beyond those required for conducting good scientific research.

ACCOUNTABILITY

The head of R & D will operate within the general guidance of some representative person or body from the parent authority. He will plan, implement, direct and justify the R & D activities and 'sell' the results to the parent authority. The heavy emphasis is on selection of the programme and seeing it is carried out and used effectively. He is then concerned with ensuring that the programme is carried out with increasing efficiency in all senses.

KNOW-HOW AND SKILLS REQUIRED

Extensive formal training in at least one of the recognised scientific or engineering disciplines is virtually essential, with some knowledge of business administration, preferably acquired formally.

Substantial experience in the supervision of the type of research concerned, or something similar and of its association with 'user' organisations.

A thorough understanding of the parent organisation's products and processes, an understanding of the principles of management planning and policy making, and a natural and acceptable approach to staff to motivate them in taking initiative to get the work done.

HUMAN RELATIONS KNOW-HOW

The selection of candidates for appointment and promotion or transfer must be ably carried out.

Plans for development and improvement of staff capabilities must be established.

The appraisal of staff at all levels is a continuous task. The ability to delegate responsibilities to subordinates liberally, but with checks to see that the delegated responsibility is being adequately held.

Selection and cultivation of relationships with 'friends' or potential 'friends' of the organisation.

Contribution to positive publication and other programmes for creating the research image of the organisation.

MANAGERIAL KNOW-HOW

The head of research:

Organises the structure of the department.

Establishes policies on recruiting, training, etc., of staff.

Determines or recommends appropriate remuneration and other incentives to personnel.

Determines or recommends the facilities and tools necessary for effective research.

Develops proper balances between basic and applied research and development, and between internal research and external research or bought know-how.

Orients specific research programmes toward the goals of greatest potential.

Sets target dates realistically for the research and objective and sees that they are met.

Develops the programme for increasing productivity.

Negotiates research and commercial agreements relevant to his research activities.

PROBLEM SOLVING

Problem solving is the basic activity of the R & D department, and the greatest development of scientific and technical ability and experience and knowledge is the biggest task of the R & D head. He must know what type of approach is likely to prove successful, whether a task can be done with the skills and facilities available or obtainable, how to carry it out – not in detail, but by virtue of what resources, at what level, are the optimum – and how much money is likely to be needed. Getting the results in a usable form is a further skill of a most difficult kind.

This may be regarded as a check list of the technical abilities and qualities required of a head of research, although they will only be met in part by any one man.

ATTRIBUTES OF RESEARCH LEADER

It emerges that a research director is in a particularly powerful situation in manipulating and getting the best out of major physical resources, and much more importantly, from the creative efforts of bodies of men of the highest intellect and ability. The danger is that he will be recognised as more powerful than he actually is so that his research workers will pay too much attention to his views on their work, perhaps with resentment, rather than merely accepting guidance as to the general path. The director has then a final duty to circumscribe his own influence and activities to enable the creativity of his staff to develop full expression.

In this chapter the importance of the creative control of the director's work has been emphasised while the major part of the book has been concerned with the individual tools available and how they should be used with caution and qualification by him.

The modern director of research, in industry, government, research associations or even the university, must aim to compound a knowledge of all these skills assembled as a creative act in a mix which accords with the particular function of his department. He also needs imagination, shrewdness, judgement, wisdom; he needs the trustworthiness and integrity that inspire confidence, the negotiating skill which brings about compromise; he needs toughness in taking decisions, aggression to further the purposes of his laboratories, and courage to choose the lesser of two evils rather than let things slide.

Finally he should desirably exercise some flair which stamps his department with an identity, making it recognisable as a unit with a reputation for excellence. These are the aims to which all research managers should aspire and in which none will wholly succeed.

SUMMARY

The process of co-operative research may be likened to orchestral players with the director as conductor, the research managers as section leaders and the researchers as skilled, creative players. The director's job is to get the best out of the players, but in doing so, to create a whole that is greater than the sum of the parts. The individual research worker must be treated as an individual creator and not 'managed' in the ordinary sense. It is important to spur the research worker to the highest scientific standards he is capable of by placing him continuously with good associates, by refusing poor standards in report writing and by placing him in positions which 'stretch' him in directions he seems to have potential for.

The distinction between leadership and power has particular relevance in the research situation, and the critical tasks of leadership include defining goals, deciding upon means, defending the organisation's integrity and the ordering of internal conflict. Different situations demand different styles of leadership – development projects with tight end dates may be more successful with a fairly 'authoritarian' approach: the so-called supportive style is probably more acceptable for more basic research. But in practice a mixture of styles will normally be required. The typical responsibilities of the head of a research department are discussed under categories of accountability, skills required, managerial know-how, and flair for problem solving.

The modern director of research requires an armoury of abilities which are desirable but never wholly met with.

References

1 *Statistics of Science & Technology 1970* (HMSO, 1970).
2 J. Jewkes, D. Sowers and R. Stillerman, *The Sources of Invention* (London: Macmillan, 1969).
3 J. Child, 'The Organisation of Innovation', *Metron* vol. 3 no. 2 (Feb 1971).
4 P. Docksey, from *First Special Report from the Select Committee on Science and Technology* (HMSO, 1972).
5 R. Edgeworth Johnstone, 'The Nature of Technological Development', *Science Journal* (Nov 1967).
6 L. B. Mohr, 'Determinants of Innovation in Organisations', *American Political Science Review*, vol. 63 (1969).
7 S. W. Becker and T. L. Whistler, 'The Innovative Organisation: a selective review of current theory and research', *Journal of Business*, vol. 40, no. 4 (Oct 1967).
8 W. Marshall, Atom No. 185, UKAEA (Mar 1972).
9 G. S. Sanders, 'Management Courses for Scientists', *Chemistry in Britain*, vol. 9, no. 1 (Jan 1973).
10 A. Hart, 'Planning for Increased Research Productivity', Symposium on Productivity and Research (Institution of Chemical Engineers, 1963).
11 *CSO Research and Development Expenditure* (HMSO, 1973).
12 OECD 'Observer', June 1970, p. 22.
13 Lord Rothschild and Sir Frederick Dainton, 'A Framework for Government Research and Development' Green Paper, Cmd 4814 (HMSO, 1971).
14 E. Mansfield, *Industrial Research and Technological Innovation* (Longman, 1969).
15 R. E. Seiler, *Improving the Effectiveness of R. and D.* (McGraw-Hill, 1965).

16 'Research & Development Expenditure: a comparison of industries', Information paper of the Centre for the Study of Industrial Innovation, 1971.

17 *Estimates of Resources Devoted to Scientific Engineering Research and Development in British Manufacturing Industry 1955* (HMSO, 1958).

18 *Persons with Qualifications in Engineering, Technology and Science 1959–68*, Studies in Technology Manpower, no. 3 (HMSO, 1971).

19 I.D.L. Ball, 'The Role of Sponsored Research Establishments', *Research and Development Journal* (Jan 1963).

20 J. G. Cox, *Scientific and Engineering Manpower and Research in Small Firms* (HMSO, 1971).

21 R. I. Cole (ed.), *Improving Effectiveness in R. & D.* (Academic Press, 1967).

22 S. Zuckerman, *The Management and Control of Research and Development*, (HMSO, 1961).

23 'Industrial Research and Development in Government Laboratories – A New Organisation for the Seventies', Ministry of Technology Green Paper (HMSO, 1970).

24 *Department of Trade and Industry Report on R. and D. 1972–73* (HMSO, 1973).

25 C. J. M. Bennett (ed.), *Organising R. and D.* (National Economic Development Office, 1972).

26 A. O. Stanley and K. K. White, 'Organising the R. & D. Function', American Management Association Research Study 72, 1965.

27 R. H. Hall, *Organisations, Structures and Processes* New Jersey: Prentice-Hall, 1972).

28 O. Katz and R. L. Kahn, *The Social Psychology of Organisations* (New York: John Wiley & Sons, 1966).

29 D. S. Pugh, D. J. Hickson and C. R. Hinings, 'An Empirical Taxonomy of Work Organisations', *Administration Science Quarterly*, vol. 14, no. 1 (Mar 1969).

30 J. D. Thomson and W. J. McEwen, 'Organisational Goals and Environment', *Administration Science Quarterly*, vol. 3, no. 1 (Feb 1958).

31 D. S. Pugh *et al.*, 'Dimensions of Organisational Structure', *Administration Science Quarterly*, vol. 13, no. 2 (June 1968).

32 R. H. Hall *et al.*, 'Organisational Size, Complexity and Formalisation', *American Sociological Review*, vol. 32, no. 6 (Dec 1967).

33 P. R. Lawrence and J. W. Lorsch, *Organisation and Environment: Managing Differentiation and Integration* (Cambridge, Mass: Harvard Graduate School of Business Administration, 1967).

34 J. Q. Wilson, 'Innovation in Organisation: notes towards a theory', in J. D. Thomson (ed.), *Approaches to Organisational Design* (University of Pittsburgh Press, 1966).

35 K. E. Knight, 'A descriptive model of the intra-firm innovation process', *Journal of Business*, vol. 40, no. 4 (Oct 1967).

36 J. Hage and M. Aiken, *Social Change in Complex Organisations* (New York: Random House, 1970).

37 Sir G. Sutherland FRS, *Report of the Working Party on Liaison between Universities and Government Research Establishments*, Cmnd 3222 (HMSO, 1967).

38 W. Marshall, 'Technical Spin-off from Nuclear Research and Development', Atom (UKAEA) no. 182 (Dec 1971).

39 *Industrial Research in Britain* (Frances Hodgson, 1972).

40 *Guide to Science and Technology in the UK* (Frances Hodgson, 1971).

41 *Industrial Research in Britain* (Harrap,   ).

42 Earl of Bessborough, 'Industrial Research and Development', Conference of Industrial Research Associations, 1973.

43 *Research Associations: the Changing Pattern* (Centre for the Study of Industrial Innovation, 1972).

44 J. Leicester, 'Industrial Progress – the true measure of Research Productivity', Symposium on Productivity in Research (Institution of Chemical Engineers, 1963).

45 P. A. F. White and S. E. Smith, 'Review of Uranium Ore Processing Research', *J. Brit. Nuc. En. Soc.* (Apr 1969).

46 J. Longrish, M. Gibbons, W. G. Evans and F. R. Jevons, *Wealth from Knowledge: Studies of Innovation in Industry* (Macmillan, 1971).

47 T. S. McCleod, *Management of Research, Development and Design in Industry* (Gower Press, 1969).

48 R. L. Latham, Senior Superintendent, Engineering,

AWRE Private Communication, 1973.

49 R. L. Latham, 'Design Methods at AWRE Aldermaston' Colloquium on Design Innovation (Inst. Elec. Engineers, 1974).

50 C. J. Beattie and R. D. Reader, *Quantitative Management in Research and Development* (Chapman & Hall, 1971).

51 M. G. Kendal (ed.), *Cost Benefit Analysis* (English Universities Press, 1971).

52 P. M. S. Jones, 'The Use of Cost Benefit Analysis as an aid in allocating Government Resources to Research and Development' Programmes Analysis Unit, P.A.U. M. 17, 1970.

53 T. W. Jackson and J. M. Spurlock, *Research and Development Management* (Dow-Jones-Irwin Inc., 1966).

54 Francis Hetman, *Society and the Assessment of Technology* (Paris: OECD 1973, available from HMSO).

55 J. W. Humble (ed.), *Management by Objectives in Action* (McGraw Hill, 1970).

56 J. W. Weale, AWRE, Private Communication, 1973.

57 H. L. Wilensky, *Organisational Intelligence: Knowledge and Policy in Government and Industry* (New York: Basic Books, 1967).

58 T. Parsons, *Structure and Process in Modern Society* (New York: The Free Press, 1960).

59 R. L. Simpson, 'Vertical and Horizontal Communications in Formal Organisations', *Administrative Science Quarterly*, vol. 14, no. 2 (Sep 1969).

60 A. Downs, *Inside Bureaucracy* (Boston: Little, Brown & Co., 1967).

61 D. C. Peltz, 'Freedom in Research', *International Science and Technology* (Feb 1964).

62 P. V. Youle 'Economy in Experimentation', Symposium on Productivity in Research (Institution of Chemical Engineers, 1963).

63 Sir George Thomson, 'Productivity in Research in Universities', Symposium on Productivity in Research (Inst. Chem. Engrs, 1963).

64 L. Metzer and J. Slater, 'Organisational Structure and the Performance and Job Satisfaction of Physiologists', *American Sociological Review*, vol., 27 no. 3 (1962).

65 Sir Ronald Holroyd, 'Productivity in Industrial Research with particular reference to research in the Chemical Industry', Symposium on Productivity in Research (Inst. Chem. Engrs., 1963).

66 *The Practice of O. & M.* (HMSO, 1965).

67 *Treasury Control of Establishments*, 5th Report of Estimates Committee (1963–64) HC 228 (HMSO, 1964).

68 *Job Evaluation: a practical gimmick* (British Institute of Management, 1971).

69 British Standard 3138: 1959. Glossary of terms in work study.

70 H. J. Pick, 'The Challenge of the new materials technology', *Metals and Materials* (Apr 1970).

71 T. Burns and G. M. Stalker, *The Management of Innovation* (Tavistock Publications, 1961).

72 M: E. Peplow, 'Morale Factors in a Research and Development Department', Symposium on Productivity in Research (Inst. Chem. Engrs., 1963).

73 J. R. P. French and B. Raven, 'The Bases of Social Power' from *Group Dynamics* New York: Harper and Row, 1968).

74 R. Tagliuri, 'Value Orientations and the Relationship of Managers and Scientists', *Administrative Science Quarterly*, vol. 10. no. 1 (June 1965).

75 L. R. Pondy, 'Organisational Conflict: Concepts and Models', *Administrative Science Quarterly*, vol. 12, no. 2 (Sep 1967).

76 H. F. Lewis (ed.), *Laboratory Planning* (Reinhold, 1962).

77 K. Guy, *Laboratory Organisation and Administration* (Butterworths, 1973).

78 Lord Robens, *Safety & Health at Work*, Cmnd 5034 (HMSO, 1972).

79 A. Etzioni, 'Dual Leadership in Complex Organisations', *American Sociological Review*, vol. 30, no. 5 (Oct 1965).

80 P. Selznick, *Leadership in Administration* (New York: Harper & Row 1957).

81 F. E. Fiedler, *A Theory of Leadership Effectiveness* (New York: McGraw-Hill, 1967).

82 *Framework for Government Research and Development*, Cmnd 5046 (HMSO, 1972).

83 *National Patterns of R & D Resources: Funds and Man-*

power in the United States (National Science Foundation, NSF 73–303, 1973).

84 *Research and Development in Industry 1971* (National Science Foundation, NSF 73–305, 1973).

Index

307